B

C000219100

Technology
For Motor Mecha

PART 3

Technology
for Motor Mechanics

PART 3 (SECOND YEAR)

SECOND EDITION

S. C. Mudd, F.I.M.I., A.M.B.I.M., M.A.E.T.

Deputy Head, Department of Technician
and Motor Vehicle Engineering,
Huddersfield Technical College

Edward Arnold

© S. C. Mudd 1972

First published 1969
by Edward Arnold (Publishers) Ltd
41 Bedford Square
London WC1B 3DQ

Second edition 1972
Reprinted 1973, 1975, 1976, 1978

ISBN: 0 7131 3277 9

Printed Offset Litho in Great Britain by
Cox & Wyman Ltd
London, Fakenham and Reading

Preface to the Second Edition

This book is intended for those student motor mechanics who have already passed the Part One examination of the City and Guilds of London Institute in Motor Vehicle Craft Studies, or similar Regional Examinations, and for those who have successfully completed the first year of the Technicians' Course.

In revising the book, the opportunity has been taken to express quantities in SI units wherever possible; otherwise the arrangement is largely unchanged from the first edition.

The material provided satisfies the requirements of the second years of the Craft Courses, and the greater part of the second year of the Technicians' Course, in the technology subject. It should also be of assistance in the workshop and science subjects, especially where fault location is involved.

Once again great emphasis has been placed on simple line diagrams and it is hoped that the material, and its presentation, will both widen the scope and increase the depth of the student's understanding of his chosen trade. It is also hoped that teachers and instructors will find the book very suitable for class use, enabling them to give much more of their time with the class to the real work of teaching.

Huddersfield   S. C. Mudd
1972

Acknowledgements

The author wishes to express his grateful thanks for the advice and active assistance so generously given by his colleagues, and by the following companies:

A.C.–Delco Division of General Motors Ltd.
Alkaline Batteries Ltd.
British Motor Corporation
Borg & Beck Ltd. (One of the Automotive Products Group)
Champion Sparking Plug Co. Ltd.
V. L. Churchill and Co. Ltd.
Dunlop Rubber Co. Ltd.
Ford Motor Company Ltd.
Girling Ltd. (Sales and Service)
Hepworth and Grandage Ltd.
Hobourn-Eaton Manufacturing Co. Ltd.
J. E. Baty and Co. Ltd.
Joseph Lucas (Sales and Service) Ltd.
J. Payen Ltd.
Lockheed Hydraulic Brake Co. Ltd. (One of the Automotive Products Group)
Rootes Group School
A. Schrader's Son (Division of Scovill Manufacturing Co.)
Serck Services
Smiths Industries Ltd. Motor Accessory Division
Solex Ltd.
S.U. Carburettor Company
Zenith Carburettor Co. Ltd.
Kismet Ltd.

Contents

ELECTRICAL TECHNOLOGY

1 Materials and Measurements

Apart from sheet-steel pressings and low-stressed nuts and bolts, almost every part of the vehicle is made from one or other of the many alloy steels. Almost every part is heat treated to improve the properties given by the alloy, and to make it more suitable for its particular function in the vehicle.

High-carbon steels

These may be divided into tool steels and cast steels. 'Tool steel' is an old classification and refers to crucible steel which contains from 1·2% to 1·4% carbon. It is very tough and is always hardened and tempered after shaping and machining. It is used for fine-edged cutting tools where little heat and load is required.

Steel castings are made from a special type of mild steel. Cast steel is a high-carbon steel and the term 'cast' refers to the fact that when it is first produced it is cast into ingots. All subsequent shaping is done by forging, rolling and machining.

High-carbon steel is fairly hard and very tough. It is difficult to weld and can only be machined well by very hard-tipped tools, or by grinding. The carbon content is between 0·7% and 1·2%, and the steel is hardened right through by hardening and tempering.

Uses

High-carbon steel is used for most tools and is usually hardened and tempered – but not to the same degree in every tool. Examples of tools for which it is used are: files, drills, reamers, cold chisels, pliers, punches, rules, scrapers and scribers. Vices are often made from this material but only the jaws are hardened and tempered, the main parts needing to be very tough rather than hard.

High-carbon steel is often used today as the basic material for the production of alloy steels.

High-tensile steel

This is any high-carbon steel which has a tensile strength of over 770 MN/m². This higher strength is not obtained by alloying but by cold rolling and other work-hardening processes. This cold-worked steel is used for large coil springs, and sometimes for very highly stressed bolts and studs, although these are now often made from alloy steels.

High-speed steels

These are alloy steels used for cutting tools. The alloy is tungsten, and tools made from this steel can stand up to much heavier cuts, and much faster cuts, than straight carbon tools, without softening, or losing their cutting edges.

ALLOYING MATERIALS

These are added to carbon steels during the production process. Their purpose is to improve the existing qualities of the steel and to add new properties. Alloy steels are much more expensive than plain carbon steels but are so much stronger and more suited to vehicle work that plain steel is seldom used in a modern vehicle. Parts made from alloy steel have a much longer life and, because the material is stronger, they can be made lighter in weight.

The most common alloying materials, and the properties they impart, are:

Nickel

This improves strength and ductility. In mild steels it improves the quality of the case-hardening process by toughening the softer core and by making the change from the high-carbon skin to the low-carbon core more gradual. This reduces the tendency of the hardened skin to chip away from the core under high impact loads.

Chromium

The addition of chromium increases both the hardness and the toughness. Very often both nickel and chromium are added to the steel, and the resulting metal, after hardening and tempering, is used for highly stressed parts such as crankshafts. As the percentage of chromium is increased, so is the resistance to corrosion and oxidation. Stainless steels are those which contain more than 12% chromium.

Tungsten
When tungsten is added, steel can be made very hard, and the tungsten also helps the steel to retain magnetism. Tungsten is used in some valve steels and for valve seats. It is also used for contact-breaker points in coil ignition systems.

Molybdenum
This has the same effects as tungsten but to a much greater degree. It provides extra hardness at high temperatures and increases the toughness during tempering operations. It also increases the resistance to acids. A nickel–chromium-molybdenum steel may be used for crankshafts and a chromium–molybdenum steel for half-shafts.

Manganese
Manganese increases the toughness of the steel and steels containing it are used where hardening is to be produced by rolling processes, i.e. it work hardens quickly to produce a very hard-wearing surface. It may also be used to make welding easier.

Cobalt
Cobalt, together with nickel and aluminium, produces a steel with excellent magnetic properties. It is difficult to magnetize but retains its magnetism over long periods. This steel is therefore used for strong permanent magnets.

When cobalt and chromium are both added to carbon steel the resulting alloy steel is air hardening and will not scale at high temperatures. It is also very corrosion-resistant and may be used for exhaust valves.

Silicon
This material is used with manganese and improves the hardening action. Silicon–manganese steel is used for road springs and some valve springs.

Vanadium

This is used with other alloys and provides extra fatigue resistance by increasing the toughness. It may be used in beam-type axles.

Aluminium

When aluminium is added to a chromium–molybdenum–carbon steel it forms a nitrogen-hardening steel known as 'Nitralloy'. Between 0·9% and 1·3% of aluminium is added. The nitride case-hardening process consists of heating the finished part for about 90 hours at a temperature of 500 °C in the presence of ammonia gas. The nitrogen of the gas reacts chemically with the iron and aluminium to form a case or skin of aluminium and iron nitride which is extremely hard. Quenching is not required and therefore distortion and cracking does not occur. This process may be used for hardening steel and iron alloy cylinder liners.

NOTE. Almost every part of the vehicle is made from an alloy steel which has been heat treated to develop its properties to suit the requirements of its use.

HEAT MUST NOT BE APPLIED DURING REPAIR WORK
OR THE PROPERTIES RESULTING FROM THE HEAT
TREATMENT WILL BE LOST

The loss of these properties will weaken the part, and could result not only in its failure but also in the death of the vehicle user.

NON-FERROUS METALS

These are metals which contain no iron.

Copper

This metal is used in its pure state for electrical components and cables because it is a very good conductor of electricity. It is also a good conductor of heat and is used in the construction of radiators, oil coolers, and interior heaters. Copper is a fairly soft and ductile metal, and is fairly resistant to corrosion. For these reasons it may be used for fuel and oil pipes. Copper is hardened by age and by vibration, but it may be annealed by heating to a cherry red and quenching in oil or water; in the annealed state it has about half the tensile strength of mild steel. Copper is also used as the basic material for a number of important alloys.

Brass

Brasses are alloys of copper and zinc. An alloy of 70% copper and 30% zinc is known as cartridge brass and is very ductile and strong. It is therefore used for deep-drawn pressings such as those for radiator tanks. Brasses which contain up to about 39% zinc can be cast or rolled but cannot be worked hot. A hot-working brass consists of 60% copper and 40% zinc and is known as Muntz metal. Brazing spelter usually consists of 50% copper and 50% zinc, and melts at about 880 °C. Brass is very easy to solder.

When nickel is added to brass it forms a material known as German silver or nickel silver. This is a strong metal which takes a very good polish. Brass may also be used for certain parts which are to be electroplated because brass forms an excellent base for the deposits. In general, brass is relatively expensive and it is often replaced in vehicle construction by the very much cheaper die-cast zinc-base alloys.

Phosphor bronze

The bronzes are alloys of copper and tin. Phosphor bronze is an alloy of copper, tin, and phosphorus which has a low coefficient of friction when used with steel. It is tough enough to withstand heavy loads. It may also have a percentage of lead added, and in this form may be used for heavy-duty bushes and bearings. With a relatively high percentage of added tin it may be used in heavy commercial vehicles for the worm wheels of rear axles, operating with a case-hardened steel worm.

Lead bronze

These alloys may also be used for bushes and bearings but this material is not as hard as phosphor bronze. One alloy consists of about 10% lead, 10% tin, and 80% copper. It is suitable for use with relatively soft steel shafts, e.g. dynamo bushes.

Aluminium

Aluminium is not used in the pure state for vehicle construction because it is too weak. Aluminium alloys, however, are now widely used. These have the general properties of being light in weight, being good conductors of heat and electricity, and, after an electrical process called anodizing, being fairly resistant to corrosion. The

best alloy for corrosion resistance is aluminium silicon. Aluminium–
manganese alloys are used in sheet form for light but strong body
panels, and aluminium–copper alloys are used for cast gearbox and
rear axle cases – where lightness, strength, resistance to shock loads,
and easy machining are important. Aluminium–silicon alloys are
used for pistons, cylinder heads, and sumps where good heat con-
duction is important as well as lightness and corrosion resistance.
Aluminium–copper alloys both age harden and work harden.

Aluminium bronze
This is an alloy of aluminium and copper which has a good resistance
to wear and heat. Parts made from this alloy are usually chill cast,
e.g. gearbox selector forks.

Tin
Tin is a very expensive metal which is usually used, as an alloying
metal, with copper and lead. Solders and white metals are examples
of such use. It is also used as a coating for steel plate, then called
'tinplate', and is corrosion resistant.

Lead
This is a weak, soft, and ductile metal used as the basic material for
a number of alloys. When combined with antimony it may be used
for battery plates. It is heavy and is not attacked by most acids. Lead
oxides are used as the plate pastes in batteries.

Zinc
Pure zinc is ductile and malleable, and is almost unaffected by corrosion in air. This is because its oxide skin forms very rapidly and
protects it from further corrosion. It is used to coat iron and steel,
e.g. galvanized iron sheets. Zinc is largely used as an alloy in the
production of brasses.

White metal
Two classes of white metal are used, being based on either tin or
lead. In vehicle engines the tin-based alloy is used because of its
higher load-carrying qualities. A very commonly used alloy is composed of 92% tin, 4% copper, and 4% antimony. These alloys have
a very low coefficient of friction when used with steel and their

melting-points are about 300 °C. In compression-ignition engines, where the bearing pressures are higher and more sustained, copper–lead alloy may be used with an outer coating of lead–tin alloy.

Antimony

This metal is used in bearing alloys to increase their hardness, and in cast alloys to produce a cleaner, i.e. more accurate, casting. This is because antimony expands slightly as it cools and solidifies.

LIMITS, FITS AND GAUGING

Limits

The motor engineer is greatly concerned with the correct mating of parts which have to operate together, whether movement occurs between them or not. In addition to considering the sizes, shapes, and materials of the parts, he must also consider the effects upon them of different operating speeds and loads, and of temperature changes. These factors all influence the designer in his choice of the tolerances to be permitted in their manufacture, and of the fits and clearances to be used to ensure their correct assembly and location.

In practice it is impossible to finish a component or part to an exact size. In many instances, to even attempt to do so would be both unnecessary and very expensive. It is, however, both possible and essential to control errors by setting the maximum and the minimum sizes permissible. These sizes are called limits, and are very important in the mating of different parts. The difference in size between the upper and the lower limit is called the tolerance.

Example

The limits of a gudgeon pin are 22·225 mm and 22·2225 mm. The tolerance is 22·225 mm minus 22·2225 mm, or 0·0025 mm.

Tolerances may be arranged completely above or below the nominal or basic size and these are called unilateral tolerances. Where the tolerance is arranged across the nominal size, i.e. both above and below the nominal size, it is called a bilateral tolerance.

Example

Assume that the nominal size of a crankpin is 50 mm and the tolerance is 0·0762 mm.

If this 0·0762 mm is permitted above the nominal size then the tolerance is unilateral. It would be written as:

$$50 \text{ mm} \begin{array}{c} +0\cdot0762 \\ -0\cdot0000 \end{array}$$

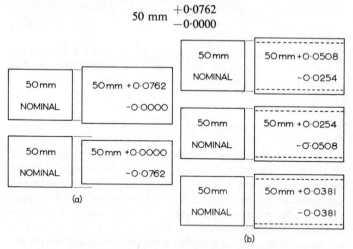

Fig. 1.1 Tolerances: (a) unilateral; (b) bilateral

If this 0·0762 mm is permitted below the nominal size then the tolerance is again unilateral and would be written as:

$$50 \text{ mm} \begin{array}{c} +0\cdot0000 \\ -0\cdot0762 \end{array}$$

If this 0·0762 mm is permitted across the nominal size then the tolerance is bilateral. Exactly how it is written will depend upon the arrangement of the tolerance across the nominal size, e.g. as:

$$50 \text{ mm} \begin{array}{c} +0\cdot0508 \\ -0\cdot0254 \end{array} \text{ or } 50 \text{ mm} \begin{array}{c} +0\cdot0254 \\ -0\cdot0508 \end{array} \text{ or } 50 \text{ mm} \begin{array}{c} +0\cdot0381 \\ -0\cdot0381 \end{array}$$

Interchangeability
There are many thousands of different components involved in the construction of motor vehicles, and many thousands of each component have to be produced. Different components have also to be manufactured in different factories. To avoid the need for further machining or fitting work during assembly or repair, the components must be interchangeable. The machine tools used in their production must not only be capable of producing quickly the large

numbers required but they must also produce each item to a high degree of accuracy, i.e. so that differences between individual components are very small. An interchangeable part is one which can be substituted for a similar part made from the same drawing. Full interchangeability is not always necessary, although many vehicle components are made in this way.

Classes of interchangeability

For changes affecting production, three classes of interchangeability are recognized:

(1) Full interchangeability. The modified or later design of part can be fitted without difficulty. Modified parts may be used to replace the older designs of the same part, and vice versa.
(2) Semi-interchangeability. The modified design of part can replace the older, but not vice versa.
(3) Conditional interchangeability. The modified design of part can replace the older after slight alterations have been made either to it or to its mating part.

Where different parts have to be mated it is most important that the tolerances of each are adhered to, and used in such a way that the desired fit or clearance is obtained. This is ensured by the use of some system of limits. Such a system may be based upon either the hole or the shaft. The hole-based systems are the most common because it is easier to vary the size of a shaft than the size of the hole, holes being produced normally by standard tools such as drills, reamers etc.

The class or type of fit is determined by the combination of (a) the maximum size limit of the shaft with the minimum size limit of the hole and (b) the minimum size limit of the shaft with the maximum size limit of the hole. If a running fit were being considered, the clearance in condition (a) would be the least permitted and in condition (b) would be the greatest permitted.

Gauging

Gauging is the use of some form of gauge to determine whether or not the features of a component are within acceptable limits. Gauging is not concerned with actual sizes.

The diameter of a crankpin could be checked by the use of a caliper type of 'go' and 'not-go' gauge. This consists of two sets of jaws, the gap between one being accurately ground to the maximum size permitted and the gap between the other being the minimum size permitted. If the 'go' jaw will pass over the crankpin and the 'not-go' will not, then the crankpin diameter is within acceptable limits. Checks would be made in more than one position and in more than one plane.

Double-ended plug gauges may be used in a similar manner to check whether or not holes are within their specified limits. Taper plug gauges may be used to check tapered holes, the gauge being

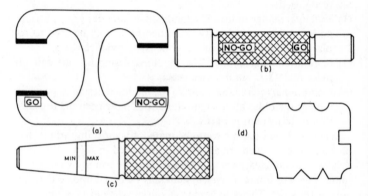

Fig. 1.2 Gauges: (a) caliper; (b) plug; (c) taper plug; (d) plate

marked or shouldered to indicate the correct depth of entry. Plate gauges may be used to check the accuracy of radii and other shapes, and narrow grooves.

External screw-thread gauges may be used in a similar manner to the 'go' and 'not-go' gauges, but must be adjustable to compensate for wear. Screw plug gauges are also available for the checking of threaded holes.

Measurement
Measurement is the determination of the size of some feature of a component, e.g. the diameter of a crankpin.

Where very small manufacturing tolerances have to be adhered to, limit gauges are not sufficiently accurate, and special equipment has to be used to take measurements. In the case of cylinder bores and pistons the sizes are often measured very carefully and the components are then divided into groups or steps of sizes within the tolerances. The correct mating of the pistons with the bores is then obtained by selecting the mating groups for the quality of fit. This is called selective assembly; it can be carried out quickly with the aid of modern inspection equipment.

In vehicle service work, worn parts have to be measured and the measurements compared with the manufacturers' specifications in order to determine (a) whether the parts are fit for further use, (b) whether they can be reconditioned and used again, and (c) whether they must be replaced by new parts.

GAUGES

Dial gauge
Construction

The dial gauge consists of a circular case which is clamped to a suitably rigid base when the instrument is in use. A spring-loaded plunger is mounted in the case, with its ends passing through the sides of the case. The movement of the plunger is magnified by a system of accurate gear trains, backlash being taken up by a small hair-spring. The total plunger movement is about 13 mm and the magnification is about one hundred and twenty-five. The gears rotate a pointer over a circular dial which can itself be rotated and clamped to the case in any position. The dial is usually graduated to read to 0·01 mm or 0·02 mm, the graduations or divisions being marked at each side of a common zero. Other dials may be graduated in thousandths of an inch or tenths of thousandths of an inch. A second and smaller pointer is often incorporated which indicates the number of complete revolutions made by the large pointer.

Use

The dial gauge in itself cannot measure a dimension – it can only measure *differences* between dimensions. If it is first set to zero on a standard thickness or diameter, however, its readings will indicate whether or not the item being checked is at the standard size or above or below it. It will also indicate how great the difference is and, if this reading is added or subtracted from the setting dimension, the actual checking dimension is obtained.

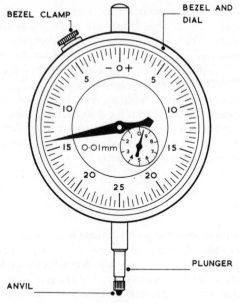

Fig. 1.3. Dial gauge

Cylinder-bore gauges employ a dial gauge fitted into a special holder or base. Different shapes of feet may be fitted to the plunger to make it more suitable for use in different situations.

Cylinder bore gauge

Construction

These are dial gauges fitted into holders specially shaped to make them convenient to use in deep bores such as those in the engine cylinder block. In the Mercer and Baty designs, the holder consists of a long handle with a plastic grip, the gauges being clamped into the upper end of the handle. The face of the gauge is therefore easily visible at all times.

A shoe and a spring-loaded plunger are permanently attached, at right angles, to the lower end of the holder, and a system of levers transmits the motion of this plunger up to the plunger of the dial gauge. The shoe has either two hardened and radiused faces or two ball bearings which provide a fixed measuring point, i.e. ensure that the shoe and plunger lie on the diameter of the bore. The plunger may be fitted with different lengths of extension rod to suit different bore diameters. The contact ends of these rods are either ball bearings or the end of the rod itself, hardened and ground hemispherical.

Use
The cylinder bores must be clean and dry. The holder is placed in the bore and an extension selected to suit the bore diameter. The

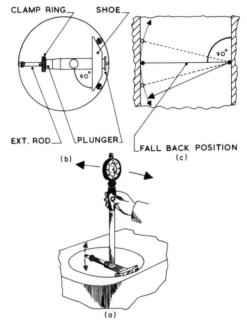

Fig. 1.4 (a) method of using; (b) plan; (c) side view

position of the rod in the plunger is then so adjusted that the opposite end of the plunger makes full contact with the cylinder wall as the holder is rocked in the bore, pivoting about the shoe faces. The rod is then locked by its clamp ring. The dial gauge is very carefully fitted into the holder in such a position that it can be read easily, and can indicate both positive and negative readings. This can be ensured by lowering the gauge until the small needle is indicating at least one full revolution of the larger needle. The gauge is then clamped into the holder.

As dial gauges are comparison indicators, they must be set to zero at a standard size. A caliper micrometer, or a setting ring gauge of the correct internal diameter, may be used. In the garage, a cylinder-bore gauge will usually be used to determine whether or not reboring is necessary and for this purpose the gauge may be zeroed on the unworn part of the top of the bore. The readings then taken will indicate the extent of the wear.

When using these gauges it is most important that the plunger should lie exactly on the diameter of the cylinder bore, and also be at a right angle to the cylinder wall. The first is ensured automatically by the shape of the shoe. The second may be checked by rocking the holder about the shoe faces; the large needle will move up to a point on the dial and then fall back. This point indicates that the plunger is at a right angle to the cylinder wall, i.e. is least extended. This would also be the set zero position when the gauge is being zeroed.

All readings are taken by gently rocking the holder in this manner and reading the scale at the point of fall back. In a worn bore, all readings should be positive, i.e. they should all indicate diameters greater than the unworn diameter and the readings show how much wear has taken place. The scale of the dials may be marked into divisions representing 0·01 mm or 0·002 mm (0·0005 in or 0·0001 in) and usually read up to 25 divisions on each side of a common zero.

When measuring the bores of a cylinder block it is usual to take six readings. These are taken in the thrust and non-thrust directions at the top, centre and bottom of each bore, and from these readings the maximum wear, taper and ovality of each bore is established. The largest reading in any position is taken to be the maximum wear, and a rebore is usually considered necessary if this reading exceeds 0·25 mm. The reboring size may be established by boring out the most worn bore until all signs of wear are removed. This bore is then measured and the nearest piston size above this new diameter becomes the final rebored and finished size. Running clearances are allowed on the piston, so the nominal size of the piston is the rebore size.

Telescopic gauges
Construction
Because of their shape, these are sometimes known as 'T' gauges. They are usually supplied in sets which provide a range of sizes. Each gauge consists of a handle and one fixed arm. The second arm is spring-loaded and is a push fit in the first arm into which it may be telescoped. The telescopic arm can be locked in any desired position by means of a knurled locking nut at the end of the handle. The end of each arm is ground spherical to suit the smallest bore the gauge can measure.

Use
Telescopic gauges are used inside bores which are too small to permit the use of internal micrometers of dial gauges. They are much more

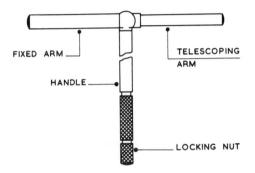

FIXED ARM

TELESCOPING
ARM

HANDLE

LOCKING NUT

Fig. 1.5 Telescopic gauge

accurate than the ordinary caliper. The telescopic arm is moved inward and locked, and the gauge head is inserted into the bore. The lock is released and the arm springs out to contact the bore wall. The head is moved until the arms are at 90° to the wall and the lock is then applied. The gauge is then withdrawn and the distance between the ends of the arms is measured by an accurate micrometer.

Small hole gauges
Construction
These gauges are designed for use in bores too small to be measured

by means of telescopic gauges, e.g. valve guides and small bushes. The gauges are supplied in sets which can cover the range of bore diameters from about 1·5 mm up to about 12 mm, or the imperial equivalents.

Each gauge consists of a tubular handle into which is screwed a tapered rod. Two steel balls are so arranged in the lower part of the

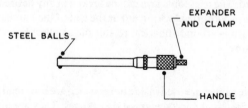

Fig. 1.6 Small hole gauge

handle that the screwing down of the rod forces the balls to move outward. A lock is fitted which enables the rod to be clamped to the handle when required.

Use

The tapered rod is slackened back and the gauge head inserted into the bore. The rod is then screwed down to force the balls to contact the sides of the bore – with the correct feel. The rod is then clamped in this position, the gauge withdrawn, and the distance across the faces of the balls measured by the use of an accurate micrometer.

Engine Construction (1)

This is the general term used to describe the assembly consisting of the following components:
(1) The block in which the cylinders are grouped.
(2) The crankcase which supports and locates the crankshaft.

To these components are attached (a) the cylinder head in which the combustion chambers are formed and which seals off the upper ends of the cylinders, (b) the inlet and exhaust manifolds, and (c) the sump which seals off the lower face of the crankcase and which, in most vehicle engines, acts as an oil tank.

Most vehicle engines are water cooled, and the cylinder block and head are therefore hollow castings. There are two main forms of cylinder block construction – the integral type in which the block and crankcase are combined, and the separate-unit type in which the two components are bolted together.

Integral construction (Fig. 2.1)
This is the simplest and cheapest form of construction and it is used for the engines of most car and light commercial vehicles. These are now all overhead-valve engines and are usually of four or six cylinder in-line design. The cylinder bores, water jackets, and crankcase are produced as a single iron casting which is very rigid and produces no problems in positioning the cylinders on the crankcase. The crankcase portion has very heavy webs which support the crankshaft and camshaft and hold them in position, the crankcase wall and the webs being ducted to direct lubricating oil to the shaft bearings. The end and lower faces of the crankcase are machined to provide mountings for the clutch and gearbox housing, the sump, and units such as oil and fuel pumps, filters, and timing-gear covers.

When the side-by-side valve arrangement was used, the valve ports and seats were cast in the cylinder block; in modern valve arrangements they are formed in the cylinder head.

Separate construction (Fig. 2.2)

This is a more complicated and expensive form of construction in which separate cylinder block castings are bolted to a single cast crankcase. Generally this form is used only for the larger engines of heavy commercial vehicles. Each cylinder block casting contains two, three or six cylinders of wear-resistant alloy iron or steel, these being known as wet liners because they are in direct contact with the cooling water. Special sealing arrangements must be made to prevent water leaking into either the cylinders or the crankcase.

The cylinder-block castings and the crankcase casting are usually made from a heavy-duty aluminium alloy. The shape of the crankcase is similar to that of the integral type and it is similarly reinforced by strong webs. Cylinders may be held in location on the crankcase by a master spigot on one cylinder in each block, or by dowels. Overhead valve arrangements are universal with this form of construction. Generally these engines are *relatively* light in weight and have a long service life.

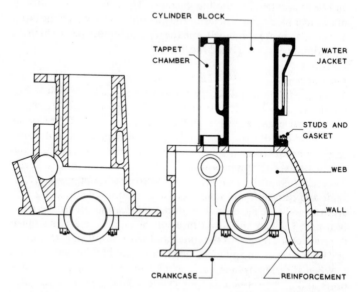

Fig. 2.1 Integral construction   Fig. 2.2 Separate construction

Separate liners

The form of cast iron which produces the most accurate casting does not provide a really long-lasting surface for cylinder bores. Modern practice is to increase the service life of the engine by fitting special sleeves or liners into the bored holes of the cylinder block. These liners are made from an alloy iron or steel and are either a press or interference fit in the block bore. They may be wet or dry types.

When a cylinder block has been reconditioned by reboring, and has reached an oversize of about 1·5 mm above its standard size, a subsequent overhaul will necessitate the fitting of liners to bring the bore size back to standard. New engines may also be lined or 'sleeved', the iron or steel alloy used for the liners being about four times as resistant to wear as the cast iron used for the cylinder block.

Types of liner

Two main types of liner are in use. These are:
(a) Wet liners – which are in direct contact with the cooling water and which are thick-walled and rigid.
(b) Dry liners – which do not contact the cooling water and which are fitted into accurately bored holes in the cylinder block.

Wet liners. These are generally used in the construction of the larger engines but are becoming popular in car engines. They have the advantage of much more efficient cooling and are simple to replace when worn beyond acceptable limits. The cylinder block is a box-like casting of iron or aluminium alloy and the liner is held in position at its upper end by a shoulder fitting into a recess in the block top. Rubber sealing rings, or a shoulder and a paper gasket, are used to seal the lower end. The top of the liner should protrude about 0·13 mm above the face of the block at all points around its circumference to obtain a good gas-tight seal. Shoulder or counter-bore seatings must be checked for both truth and cleanliness before the liners are fitted, and rectified if necessary. Care must be taken not to rotate the crankshaft when the cylinder head has been removed – unless the liners have been clamped down. This precaution will prevent the seals being damaged by accidental moving of the liners.

Dry liners. These are made in two forms and differ in their fit into the bore in the cylinder block. Both are fitted into accurately machined bores and there must be no areas where a close contact is not made between the bore and the outside surface of the liner. If there are areas of reduced contact, local hot spots will occur and result in more rapid wear and possible piston seizure, air in the gap acting as a heat insulator. These areas may be seen as blue or brown patches on the working surfaces of the liner.

Slip-fit liners. These are dry liners which are just free in their bores. These types are finish-machined internally and externally and have the advantage that they can be replaced without removing the engine from the chassis. They are held in position by a flange and recess and must stand proud of the block face by 0·13 mm to 0·2 mm when installed. This is an important check which must always be carried out to ensure that the sealing gasket is gripped evenly by the liner flange.

Interference-fit liners. These are roughly finished to size internally and are finished to about 0·05 mm above the bore size of the block externally. They must be oiled or greased externally and carefully pressed into the block bore by means of a special liner press. This must also be used when withdrawing a liner, and the block bore exposed must be carefully cleaned and checked for roundness, parallelism and size before installing a new liner. If necessary, the

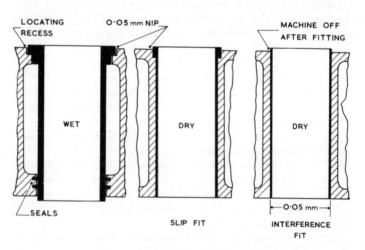

Fig. 2.3 Liners

block bore must be machined oversize and a liner of oversize out-side diameter fitted. The liners should be fitted alternately and not in numerical sequence to reduce the possibility of distorting the block. When all the liners have been installed the block top should be lightly machined and a slight chamfer filed at the top of each bore to remove the very sharp edge left. Connecting-rod slots, if required, may be cut in the lower end of each liner at this point.

The bores of the liners are then finish-ground or honed to their exact sizes. This operation is left to the last in order to correct any slight distortion caused by the pressing-in operations.

Core plugs

These are also known as Welch plugs, and as expansion plugs.

Function. When cylinder blocks and heads are cast, the shapes of the interior cavities are obtained by the use of hard-baked sand cores. Once the molten metal has cooled and solidified these sand cores must be broken up and then removed through holes in the outer walls of the water jackets. After machining, these holes must

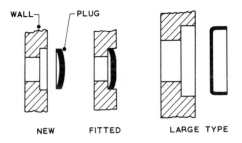

Fig. 2.4 Core plugs

be made watertight, against pressures of up to 83 kN/m², by fitting core plugs into machined recesses. The core plugs are usually dished, thin, steel discs, the edges of which are parallel to, and a close fit in, the recess.

Fitting. The recess is cleaned and dried and coated with a jointing compound. The plug is fitted into the recess, convex side outward, and firmly pressed home. It is then hammered until the convex outer face is almost flat, this action expanding the edges of the plug to make a watertight seal in the recess. The plug is left slightly convex when fitted to allow for a slight expansion later should a small leak develop in service.

It is important that the plug should not be over expanded. Normally two or three sharp blows are sufficient. Over-expanding results in the plug being slackened in the recess and so leaking.

Removal. Defective core plugs may be removed by driving an old centre punch through the middle of the plug and prising it from the recess. It may be necessary to first drill a thicker type of plug.

THE CYLINDER HEAD

This is an iron or aluminium-alloy casting of complicated shape which, in conjunction with the cylinder head gasket, seals off the tops of the cylinders. Cylinder heads may be permanently attached to the cylinders, or be detachable, and include the combustion chambers and their water jackets.

Fixed heads

In these types the cylinder head and barrel are made either as a one-piece casting in iron or as a steel barrel which has a cylinder head in aluminium alloy secured to it. In both forms the work involved in servicing the valves is made much more difficult and special equipment has to be used. For these reasons the fixed-head construction has generally been replaced by the detachable-head type, although supercharged, four-stroke diesel engines are in service using fixed heads. The advantage in these engines is that the fixed head makes pressure sealing much easier.

Detachable heads

In these designs the cylinder head is secured to the block by studs which pass through the head, nuts being used to tighten the head down upon a copper and asbestos, or thin steel, gasket which makes a gas-tight seal.

In side-valve engines the head casting may be of cast aluminium alloy, which is a better conductor of heat than cast iron, and allows the use of higher mixture compression. Where overhead valves are used, the cylinder head is complicated by the positioning of the valve ports and seats, the valve guides, the screwed holes for spark plugs, and the combustion chambers and water jackets. These heads are usually of cast iron but may also be of cast aluminium alloy.

Valve seat inserts
When aluminium alloy is used for the cylinder-head casting the valve seats and guides, and the threaded portion for the spark plug, may be made from a harder material which has the same coefficient of expansion as the material of the casting. These inserts may be made from aluminium bronze, and they may be screwed, shrunk, or peined into the casting.

When the cylinder head is made from cast iron, the valve seats and the screwed holes for the spark plugs may be machined directly

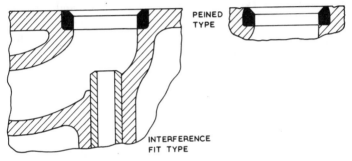

Fig. 2.5 Valve seats inserts

in the casting. In some engines, however, special seat inserts are fitted which have a much longer service life. These inserts are usually shrunk or peined into recesses in the cylinder head, and are made from a nickel–chromium steel which has the same coefficient of expansion as the iron but is much stronger and harder.

Head gaskets
These are usually formed from two stampings of thin sheet copper separated by a layer of clay and asbestos. The inner edges of the various holes through the gasket are rolled over or lined to make gas- and water-tight seals.

Some modern gaskets of this type have one face of thin sheet steel, steel also being used for the linings of the holes sealing the combustion chambers – where increased heat resistance is desirable.

This type is particularly suitable for use with cylinder heads of aluminium alloy because these heads corrode much less when in contact with steel than when in contact with copper.

A third type of gasket used for high-compression engines is the corrugated steel type. In these the sealing is done by corrugations which can flex slightly, and the general incompressibility of the gasket reduces the tendency of the head to become distorted.

Generally a copper and asbestos gasket may, as a temporary measure only, be used to replace a steel gasket. A steel gasket must not be used to replace a copper and asbestos type – unless this is permitted by the engine manufacturer.

When new, all of these types of gasket may be coated by a special form of varnish. This is intended to flow, under heat and pressure, into any small surface irregularities to provide a good initial seal. Steel gaskets must always be coated with this varnish for sealing purposes. The varnish also acts as a rust preventive.

Gasket fitting

As the cylinder-head gasket is used to provide a gas-tight seal between the cylinder block and its head – in spite of small surface irregularities – it is essential that the following precautions be taken when fitting the cylinder head:

(1) The cylinder head and the block surfaces must be clean and flat. All loose dirt and traces of water and oil must be removed. The block surface must be checked to make sure that it has not lifted at the roots of the cylinder-head studs.

(2) The best possible dressing for a gasket, where a special varnish is not specified, is a thin smear of clean grease over all the surfaces. Do not use an ordinary gasket cement or jointing compound as this will harden and then break up under the influence of pressure and temperature changes. Gasket varnish is not the same as jointing compound in its action.

(3) Handle the gasket carefully to avoid creasing the metal and breaking the asbestos filling.

(4) Tighten the cylinder-head nuts to their correct torque loading, and in their correct sequence. This is to ensure a good·seal, and it also reduces the possibility of gasket failure and head distortion. The correct sequence is given in workshop manuals; in general, the nuts are given a preliminary tightening by starting

in the centre and working outward in both directions alternately across the head. This sequence is very important and must be followed during the final tightening to the correct torque loading, and during any subsequent tightening operations after a period of running. Cast-iron cylinder heads should be tightened down when the engine is at its normal running temperature, and aluminium-alloy heads when cold.

The term 'torque loading' refers to a force being applied at a distance from the nut. At present torques are specified in pounds feet (lbf ft) or kilogram metres (kgf m) but this may be changed to newton metre (N m).* In practice a special torque-load wrench is used in which the required loading is pre-set. This cannot then be

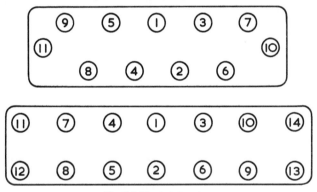

Fig. 2.6 Head tightening

exceeded except by overruling the break mechanism. In another type of torque wrench the pointer or dial gauge indicates the torque being applied.

The correct torque loadings of all the important nuts and studs are given in the workshop manuals, and these should be looked up as required. High-tensile steel studs are generally loaded about half as much again as mild steel bolts of the same diameter. Bolts, etc. having coarse threads are subjected to higher torque loadings than those of the same diameter but having finer threads. All torque loadings are increased as the stud or bolt diameters are increased. Average values for cylinder-head nuts or studs are between 54 N m

* See Appendix.

and 108 N m; for big-end bolts between 47 N m and 82 N m; and
for main-bearing nuts between 40 N m and 136 N m.

NOTE. Never guess what the torque loading should be; always
check, and always use the torque wrench in the correct manner.

Combustion chambers

The combustion chamber is the space into which most of the mixture
of petrol vapour and air is forced towards the end of the compression stroke, and in which it is ignited. The shape of the chamber has
a very great influence upon the power output and performance of
the engine, and it must be so designed that the speed of the spread
of the flame is strictly controlled. It is essential that, when the mixture
is first ignited by the spark plug, a very rapid burning of the mixture
occurs. The rate of burning must then be slowed to produce a
smooth and powerful power stroke as the piston passes over top
dead centre (T.D.C.). The rate must then be increased to burn the
remaining portion of the mixture before the exhaust valve is opened.

This final portion of mixture to be burned is often called 'end gas'
and it must be kept relatively cool to avoid 'detonation' or 'pinking'.
Detonation is the instantaneous combustion of the end gas and
results from the gas being subjected to temperatures and pressures
above those normal for a combustion chamber of that design. Detonation always occurs *after* the mixture has been ignited in the
usual way by the spark plug. Normally the flame spreads in a fairly
steady sequence but the rate of travel increases towards the end of
combustion. The end gas is therefore subjected to pressure and to
radiated heat and, if for some reason the temperature of the end gas
becomes too high, it will burn instantaneously and not progressively.
This instantaneous combustion results in an uncontrolled and very
rapid rise in pressure which is made evident by a knocking sound in
the chamber. The sound is produced by the pressure shock wave
striking the piston crown, and this can cause damage to the piston
and the bearings if allowed to continue over a long period. Detonation wastes petrol and reduces the power output.

Pre-ignition

Another form of uncontrolled combustion may occur – towards the
end of the *compression* stroke. This is called 'pre-ignition' because
the mixture is ignited *before* the spark occurs at the spark plug. Pre-

ignition usually tries to make the engine reverse its direction of rotation and therefore results in abnormal stresses being imposed on the
pistons, connecting rods and bearings; this may cause serious
damage. Pre-ignition is generally caused by white-hot particles of
metal or carbon, instead of the spark, igniting the mixture.

The degree of control exerted over the speed of travel of the flame
depends upon the shape of the combustion chamber. This in turn
depends upon the position of the valves and ports, the position of
the sparking plug in relation to the valves, and the shape of the
piston crown.

Side valve (SV) chamber
This design has a turbulence head and the inlet port is arranged at a
tangent to the cylinder bore. The volumetric efficiency is not very

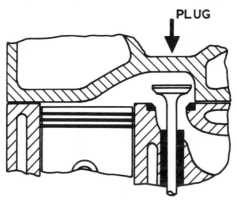

Fig. 2.7 Side valve chamber

high because of the number of direction changes to which the mixture is subjected on its way to the cylinder – and this cannot be increased by using larger inlet ports and valves without increasing the
length and weight of the cylinder-block assembly. The flame has a
long travel, and the heat losses in the chamber are fairly high because
it has a larger surface area in relation to its volume than other shapes
of chamber. If overcooling occurs the petrol economy is much
reduced.

Side-valve designs were used successfully for many years but
have been replaced by overhead designs which permit the use of a

much higher degree of compression, i.e. higher compression ratios, before the onset of detonation.

Overhead valve (OHV) chamber
This design has the valves arranged in a line above the cylinders. It is a simple design which is easy to service, and large inlet valves and ports are used. The volumetric efficiency is higher than that of the side-valve designs, and the ports are tangential to the bores. This

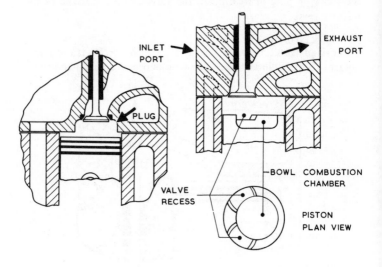

Fig. 2.8 Overhead valve chamber   Fig. 2.9 Cross flow head

provides mixture swirl, and extra turbulence is provided by placing the combustion chamber off centre in relation to the bore, the mixture being directed from the cylinder into the combustion chamber at the end of the compression stroke. This second form of turbulence is called 'squish'. The flame travel is short and detonation is less likely to occur.

Hemispherical OHV
This is a high-performance design and the valve-operating gear is both complicated and expensive. It is not possible to obtain 'squish'

but adequate turbulence is obtained by good port design and large inlet valves. Flame travel is short and it is possible to use high compression ratios.

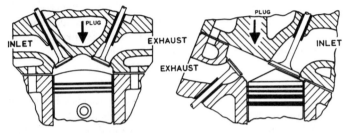

Fig. 2.10 Hemispherical overhead valve

Fig. 2.11 Overhead-valve inlet and side-valve exhaust

OHV inlet and SV exhaust

This design is an approximate hemispherical type with large inlet valves, and is fully machined. Flame travel is short and 'squish' provides good plug scour, i.e. the gas movement keeps the plug points clean. High performance and good fuel economy result from the use of this form of combustion chamber.

THE PISTON

The piston has three main functions. These are:
(1) To act as a movable gas-tight plunger in the cylinder during the induction, compression and exhaust strokes.
(2) To convert the expansion pressure of the burning mixture into a force which is transmitted to the crankshaft by the connecting rod during the power stroke.
(3) To form a guide and a bearing for the small end of the connecting rod, and to take the side thrust caused by the angularity of the crankpin and connecting-rod assembly.

Operating conditions

The normal operating temperature of the piston crown in a petrol engine is between 200° C and 250° C. The pressures acting upon the piston vary between the strokes, 1240 kN/m² being an average value over the four strokes while the maximum pressure may be about 5500 kN/m^2. These pressures are all increased as the compression ratio is increased.

Under these temperatures and pressures the piston has to withstand being accelerated to speeds of about 15 metres per second, stopped, and then returned at these high speeds. The side thrust of the piston upon the cylinder wall, during the power stroke, must also be considered, and should not exceed about 170 kN/m^2.

Construction

The piston shape is that of a cylinder, sealed at one end. The piston and connecting rod are fastened together by the gudgeon pin. The top part of the piston is termed the crown and this may be flat, convex or concave, according to the shape desired for the combustion chamber, and for the compression ratio needed. Special shapes may be used for special purposes, e.g. two-stroke and compression-ignition engines. The crown and the gudgeon pin bosses are reinforced to enable them to resist high pressures and forces, but the crown must not retain too much heat or detonation will be caused. Excessive heat must not be allowed to flow from the crown down into the skirt or distortion, and possibly a partial seizure, may be caused.

Cast-iron rings are fitted into grooves machined in the piston sides to make the piston a gas-tight fit in its bore – in spite of the necessary differences in size between them.

Materials

The following materials are used in piston construction:
(a) Cast iron.
(b) Aluminium alloys.
(c) Steel alloys.
(d) Combinations of different materials for different parts, e.g. a cast-iron crown and an aluminium-alloy skirt.

Cast-iron pistons

These pistons expand at about the same rate as the cylinder bore and their clearances can therefore be small. A good gas-tight seal is maintained and piston slap does not occur when the piston is cold. Oil consumption is slight. Cast iron is strong in compression, and has a hard-wearing surface, so bore and piston life in service is fairly long. Unfortunately cast iron is heavy and this limits the operating speed of the engine and the speed with which it responds to changes in throttle position. Cast iron is not a good heat conductor and cast-iron pistons normally operate at temperatures of between 300 °C and 400 °C. This limits the compression ratios which may be used, because the higher temperatures make detonation occur at lower cylinder pressures. These are the reasons why cast iron has been replaced by aluminium alloys for most vehicle engines, although a few commercial vehicle engines are using a new form of cast iron which is lighter and stronger than the normal iron, and which has a longer life than both the aluminium-alloy piston and the older cast-iron piston.

Aluminium-alloy pistons

These pistons have the great advantages of being light in weight and of being good conductors of heat. The weight-saving makes possible much higher engine speeds, and the quicker dissipation of heat makes possible the use of higher compression ratios without detonation. More power is therefore produced from the burning of a given weight of petrol. The cooler piston crown also results in less carbonization of the engine lubricating oil.

Aluminium-alloy pistons expand at a greater rate than their bores and therefore they must have a larger clearance than cast-iron types. This would result in piston slap when the piston is cold, so these types are designed in such a way that they are not a slack fit when cold, but cannot expand sufficiently to seize in the bore when hot.

Aluminium-alloy pistons are both hardened and toughened, and may be sand cast or die cast. They are produced in two main forms and are known as split-skirt or solid-skirt types. Most modern engines are fitted with the solid-skirt type of piston.

Split skirt. In these types the piston is ground oval and is split on the larger diameter at the non-thrust side. This results in a piston which is a close fit in its bore when cold – so reducing or obviating piston slap. As the piston absorbs heat, and expands, the split is closed slightly and so seizure is avoided. These types of piston are often used as replacements when the engine is reconditioned.

Solid skirt. The solid-skirt pistons are usually ground both oval and tapered. This is because the crown expands more than the skirt and the expansion is greater parallel to the gudgeon pin than at right angles to it. As the piston absorbs heat and expands it becomes both

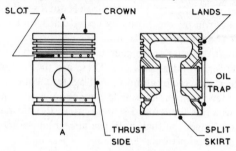

Fig. 2.12 Split skirt (on right, section across A-A)

round and parallel. These types are usually about 0·05 mm to 0·07 mm oval at the skirt and 0·18 mm to 0·28 mm oval at the crown.

In piston design, the heat flowing from the crown to the skirt must be limited to avoid distortion. This limitation is obtained by the use of slots which are cut between the head and the skirt at the thrust side. If the skirt is split this makes it more flexible also. Most variations in piston construction are concerned with controlling the heat

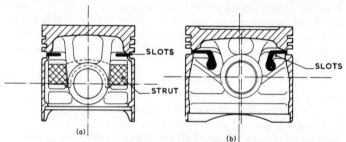

Fig. 2.13 Solid skirt: (a) strutted; (b) W design

flow inside the piston to make possible the use of small clearances.

Another type of piston is called the 'slipper piston'. In this the skirt is so reduced that only the two bearing surfaces are left, the thrust side being the larger. Both faces may also be pierced by holes to reduce oil drag. These types are very light and their frictional losses are about three-quarters of those of conventional pistons.

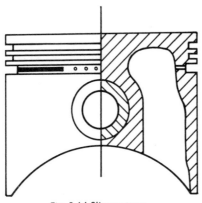

Fig. 2.14 Slipper type

Piston coatings
Aluminium-alloy pistons have not the wear resistance of cast-iron types and are therefore often given a coating of tin or aluminium oxide. A very thin coating, about 0·005 mm or five thousandths of a millimetre, provides a highly polished surface, with very little friction, which is much less liable to scuffing or partial seizure during running-in.

Another process often used is electroplating the piston with aluminium oxide. The resulting skin is very hard wearing, and the gudgeon-pin bores and ring grooves also benefit.

Coated pistons may be given a second treatment by coating them with colloidal graphite in water. The very small particles of graphite remain embedded in the surface after drying and so reduce friction between the piston and its bore. After this treatment the piston appears black, the graphite gradually being worn away as the surfaces are bedded into each other.

Piston clearances
In practice, the clearances are allowed for by the piston manufacturer, and the cylinder bores are finished to the nominal size stamped upon the piston. Most engine manufacturers grade the cylinder

bores into four or five grades, and grade pistons in a similar way –
working on the major diameter of the piston. A grade-two piston
is then fitted into a grade-two bore, the grade covering a tolerance
of between 0·005 mm and 0·010 mm (or between 5 and 10 thousandths of a millimetre).

Generally cast-iron pistons and split-skirt aluminium-alloy pistons require a clearance in the bore of 0·007 mm per 10 mm of bore
diameter, a greater clearance being required towards the crown.
Solid-skirt aluminium-alloy pistons generally require larger clearances, usually between 0·007 mm and 0·014 mm per 10 mm of bore
diameter.

Piston rings
Function
Piston rings have the following functions:
(1) To maintain a gas-tight seal between the piston and the cylinder
    wall under all normal temperatures, pressures and piston speeds.
(2) To prevent the passage of lubricating oil up to the combustion
    chamber.
(3) To transfer heat from the piston crown to the cooled cylinder
    walls.

Types
All types of piston ring transfer heat to some extent, but they are
classified by their major function of either gas sealing or oil controlling. Rings which are used to make the piston a gas-tight fit are
called compression rings, and those which prevent oil being passed
up to the combustion chambers and burned are called oil-control or
scraper rings.

Terms used
Radial pressure. This is the outward spring of the ring which holds
it in contact with the cylinder walls. The radial pressure must be
high enough to prevent gas leakage or blow-by but not so high that
increased frictional wear is caused. Most piston rings exert the same
radial pressure at every point around their circumference but some
rings exert a higher pressure at two points. These are at the ends of
the rings and at a point diametrically opposite. This form of radial
pressure is arranged to reduce ring flutter.

Side clearance. This is the clearance between the ring and the top or bottom of its groove. Side clearance must be large enough to allow the ring to move freely in the groove but not so large that it will allow the ring to pump lubricating oil up to the combustion chamber. The usual side clearance for cast-iron pistons is 0·0381 mm and for aluminium-alloy pistons is between 0·0508 mm and 0·0762 mm.

Working gap. This is the distance between the ends of the ring when it is fitted in the bore, the gap being necessary to allow for the expansion of the ring when heated. This gap is usually about 0·0305 mm for each 10 mm of cylinder-bore diameter but may be larger for high-speed air-cooled engines. It is always better to allow too much clearance at this point than too little.

Ring flutter. This is a fault where the ring seals adequately at low speeds but fails to do so at higher speeds. The ring takes up a central position *on the piston* instead of in the bore, so permitting blow-by or causing the eventual fracture of the ring. Flutter is reduced by careful attention to the radial pressure, the side clearances and the ring width, these being design and not service considerations.

Construction

Piston rings are made from an alloy cast iron of close grain, and are often centrifugally cast. The tensile strength of the material is between 250 MN/m^2 and 460 MN/m^2 and it is sufficiently elastic for the ring to be opened to pass over the piston crown when being fitted, and to press against the cylinder walls when fitted into its groove.

The ring has a gap in its circumference. This allows for the necessary radial expansion and compression, the ring being made in such a way that it is circular only when fitted into the bore. Radial pressure may be obtained by (a) form casting, (b) heat forming and (c) hammering or peining.

Compression rings

These are designed to pass heat from the piston crown to the cylinder walls, and to make the piston a gas-tight fit in the cylinder bore in spite of the essential clearance between the two. Compression rings may be square or rectangular in section, special sections being used to obtain special effects or properties. The radial pressure is usually between 70 kN/m² and 140 kN/m² and the rings are a close fit in the piston grooves.

The plain compression rings are intended for normal use, and in modern engines they are usually chromium plated on their outer faces. In engines which are prone to scuffing, the rings may be coated

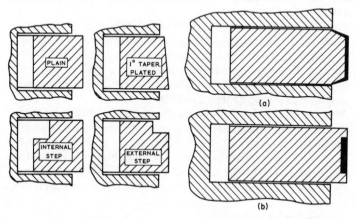

Fig. 2.15 Compression
rings

Fig. 2.16 (a) Chromium-plated ring;
(b) molybdenum-coated ring

with molybdenum. This provides a hard-wearing but porous surface which retains oil. The taper and internally stepped rings are intended to provide a quicker bedding-in. The internally stepped ring tilts in such a way that its bottom corner does most of the work – the pressure increasing as the contact area is reduced. Similarly in the taper section ring the reduced contact area increases the pressure initially and then reduces it to the normal value as the ring is bedded into the bore. The externally stepped rings are used in part worn cylinders to clear the unworn top ridge, i.e. these are 'ridge dodgers'.

Scraper rings

The main purpose of these rings is to reduce excessive consumption of engine lubricating oil by scraping the excess oil from the cylinder walls during each downward stroke of the piston. Scraper rings have little or no effect on the gas-tightness of the piston, although they do pass some heat from the piston to the cylinder walls.

Scraper rings are made in different shapes of cross-section, but all exert a higher radial pressure on the cylinder walls than compression rings. This is usually arranged by the reduction of the area of the contact face of the ring. It is very important that the rings be fitted with their scraping edges to the bottom of the bore, and that the oil be passed through the piston and returned to the sump.

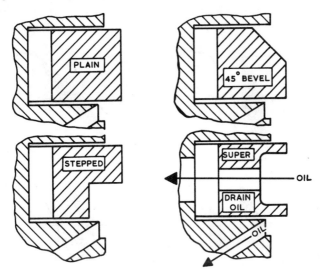

Fig. 2.17 Scraper rings

The plain ring is a mild scraper which is fitted at the bottom of the skirt and exerts a radial pressure of about 100 kN/m^2. The stepped scraper has a smaller face area and therefore exerts a higher pressure on the cylinder, usually 200 kN/m^2. The step must be fitted to the bottom of the piston. The bevelled scraper is similar in action to the stepped type but the bevelled face slides over the oil on the upward stroke. The radial pressure is reduced as the face area increases with wear. These types are usually used in the larger diesel engines. The slotted rings have two scraping edges and pass the oil back through themselves as well as the piston.

The radial pressure of slotted rings is between 200 kN/m^2 and 300 kN/m^2 and these types are used in modern high-speed petrol engines.

If higher radial pressures are required, more elastic materials must be used and more complicated shapes of section (see ApEx ring on page 40).

Ring gaps
The gap in the piston ring is necessary to allow the ring to exert a radial pressure on the cylinder walls, and to allow for the expansion

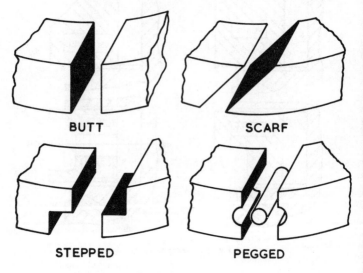

BUTT   SCARF

STEPPED   PEGGED

Fig. 2.18 Ring gaps

of the ring when heated. The working gap is the one of most concern to the mechanic, and this is checked by placing a feeler gauge in the gap when the ring is fitted in the bore. This gap will be about 0·23 mm in most car engines. In some high-performance engines the free gap must also be checked to make sure the ring has the required degree of elasticity, the gap being checked when the ring is free of radial pressure.

Many different shapes of gap have been used, the butt and scarf joints being the most popular today. These are simple to produce and check. The pegged gap is used to prevent the rings rotating in their grooves. This is necessary in two-stroke designs where the ring ends might foul the ports in the cylinder, and in some four-stroke engines where the cylinders have clearance slots for the connecting rods machined from the bottoms of the cylinders. Some modern engines have a ring with an integral peg which is fitted into a slot in the ring groove.

All these various gap shapes are attempts to allow for the expansion of the ring without causing excessive blow-by. In some engines special rings have to be employed to suit the particular operating conditions of the piston. One of these, which is used as a compression ring, has no gap as such but is slotted to form two or three sections in a similar manner to that of a key ring. This is the 'Clupet' ring which has been very effective in worn bores.

Special rings

Generally these are only used after the pistons, rings and cylinder bores of an engine have had considerable use. Wear will have resulted in the loss of compression and power, and in increased consumption of fuel and lubricating oil. The piston-to-bore clearances will have increased, the bores will have worn both oval and tapered, and wear on the outer faces of the piston rings will have resulted in their radial pressure being reduced.

Fitting new rings of the normal type will be of little use under these conditions, so steel rings of special construction are used. The ring grooves must be cleaned out and the sides machined flat before the special rings can be fitted. These are arranged to fill the ring groove from top to bottom – to stop ring pumping of the lubricating oil – and also to exert a high radial pressure to provide gas tightness in spite of the ovality of the bore. These rings can be used in bores which are up to 0·3 mm oval, and they may extend engine life by about 20 000 km.

The Cords ring consists of a series of dished spring-steel rings which must be grouped in pairs.

The Dua-flex ring consists of flat spring-steel rings which are forced outward by an expander spring, and forced to fill the groove by a second expander spring. It can also be used in diesel engines.

The ApEx type of ring is a more recent design which is also used as original equipment in many modern high-speed petrol engines. This is because these engines deliver large quantities of oil to the cylinder bores and only a high-pressure ring can prevent excessive oil consumption under these conditions. The ApEx ring consists of

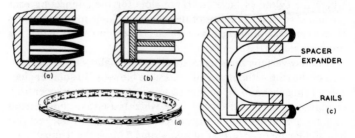

SPACER
EXPANDER

RAILS

Fig. 2.19 Special rings: (a) Cords; (b) Dua-flex; (c) and (d) ApEx

an abutment type of spacer and expander, which is independent of groove radial depth, and two steel rails with hard chromium outer faces.

Coated rings
Rings are usually given a coating which is soft and porous. This absorbs and retains oil, so reducing wear and scuffing during the bedding-in process. Tin, iron oxide and iron manganese phosphate are commonly used coating materials. Coated rings last about twice as long as uncoated rings.

The gudgeon pin
Function
The functions of the gudgeon pin are to:
(a) Connect the piston to the small end of the connecting rod.
(b) Support the small end of the connecting rod and also allow it to pivot in relation to the piston.
(c) Transfer the force of the expanding gases from the piston to the connecting rod.

Construction
The gudgeon pin is a cylindrical piece of case-hardened or fully-hardened alloy steel which is made hollow to reduce weight. The

outer surface is accurately ground to size and is given a very fine finish. The pin must resist wear and shock loads in addition to the double-shear forces to which it is normally subjected.

Types

Gudgeon pins may be classed as floating or clamped types.

Floating type. In these the pin is free to move in a phosphor-bronze bush mounted in the eye of the small end of the connecting rod. The bush is an interference fit in the rod, and the pin is usually a push fit in the bush and a thermal fit in the piston. The lateral movement

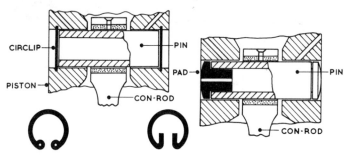

Fig. 2.20 Fully floating (circlip)   Fig. 2.21 Fully floating (end pad)

of the pin in the piston must be limited to prevent scoring of the cylinder bore. This may be done by the use of end pads of phosphor-bronze or aluminium, or by fitting circlips into grooves machined in the outer ends of the pin bores in the piston.

In some modern engines the gudgeon pin is an interference fit in the small end of the connecting rod, and an easy fit in the piston.

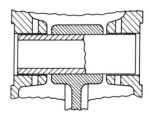

Fig. 2.22 Interference-fit type

Clamp types. In these the small end of the connecting rod is slotted and is fitted with a clamp bolt. At the centre of the length of the pin is machined a groove which allows the clamp bolt to centralize the pin at the same time as it clamps it firmly in the rod. This type is

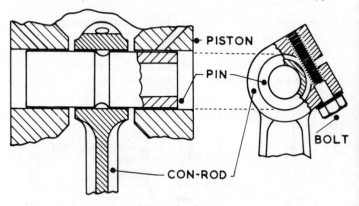

Fig. 2.23 Clamp type

usually used with alluminium-alloy pistons, long bearing surfaces being provided in the bosses of the gudgeon pin. In some modern engines the gudgeon pin is very often a thermal fit in the piston instead of a push fit, i.e. the pin can only be moved when the piston is heated to about the temperature of boiling water.

3   Engine Construction (2)

THE CRANKSHAFT

Function

The function of the crankshaft is to convert the reciprocating motion of the piston into a rotary motion, i.e. to convert the downward thrust of the piston into a turning motion or torque which can be used to drive the road wheels. The crankshaft also drives the camshaft and supports the flywheel, and indirectly drives the electrical generator and distributor, the lubricating oil pump, and the water pump and air fan of the cooling system.

Operating conditions

The maximum speed of the crankshaft is usually between 4000 and 6000 revolutions per minute. Each power stroke may produce a load on the crankshaft of about two tonnes, the main and big-end journals operating under pressures of about $14\,000$ kN/m^2. The lubricating oil temperature, i.e. bearing temperature, is usually between $50\,°C$ and $110\,°C$.

Construction

The crankshaft is probably the most highly stressed part of the vehicle and it must be made very stiff and tough to resist the very large bending and twisting forces imposed upon it. Most crankshafts are one-piece units but the crankshafts of some motor-cycle and aircraft engines are built-up assemblies.

The shape of the crankshaft is related to the number and the arrangement of the cylinders, but usually consists of a number of main journals which all rotate about the same axis or centre line. Crankpins are arranged between these main journals, at the same distances from the centre line, and are connected to the journals by webs. The crankpins are, as far as possible, arranged so as to counterbalance each other across the axis of the shaft, and weights may be fitted to the webs to counterbalance the weights of the crank-pins and the big-ends of the connecting rods. One, or two, big-ends are attached to each crankpin.

The crankwebs are drilled to direct high-pressure lubricating oil from the main journals to the crankpins, thus cooling the bearings as well as reducing friction and wear. Special oil-sealing arrangements must be made to prevent the escape of this oil from each end of the crankshaft.

Whip. A rotating shaft has a tendency at high speeds for its centre to be deflected by centrifugal force. This deflection is called 'whip' and it is reduced either by making the shaft stiffer and heavier or by using more supporting main bearings.

Throw. The distance between the centre of the crankshaft and the centre of the crankpin is termed the 'throw' of the shaft. The throw is equal to half the stroke of the piston.

Materials

Crankshafts may be forgings of a high-grade alloy steel, or castings of a special form of cast iron. In both cases the wearing surfaces must be hardened to resist wear, the heat treatment used being dependent upon the material. The steel shaft usually contains nickel, chromium, molybdenum, and occasionally aluminium. The cast-iron shaft has the alloys molybdenum and copper, or molybdenum and chromium, and is much cheaper, lighter in weight, and more wear resistant than the steel shaft. It also needs less machining.

Firing orders

The mixture of petrol and air should be so distributed between the cylinders that the same *mass* of mixture is induced into every cylinder. In practice this even distribution is not obtained because the changes in direction and velocity of the mixture, as it flows through the manifolding, make less mass of mixture available to some cylinders. The mixture strength also varies between cylinders for the same reasons.

The induction strokes of a multi-cylinder engine do not take place in numerical order but in a special sequence which is used to reduce the number of direction and velocity changes in the flow of the mixture. In this way the cylinders are able to induce approximately the same masses of mixture, i.e. the distribution of the mixture is made more even. The particular sequence used depends upon the number and arrangement of the cylinders, and upon the shape of the crankshaft. More than one sequence may be possible, but the induction strokes are usually arranged to occur alternately between the front and rear halves of the engine. These sequences are called firing orders and in some of them two cylinders in one half of the engine may fire in succession. This prevents the unwinding of the crankshaft between power strokes and so reduces the effect of the torsional vibration upon the shaft. The arrangement of the cam pairs around the circumference of the camshaft determines the firing order from a practical point of view.

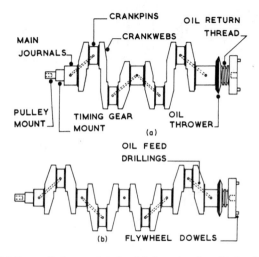

Fig. 3.1 Four-cylinder crankshafts: (a) three-bearing; (b) five-bearing

Crankshaft types

Four cylinders

The most commonly used type of crankshaft is that with four cylinders in line. Three or five main bearings are employed and the crank throws are all in the same plane. Pistons one and four will be at top dead centre together, although on different strokes, while pistons two and three will be at bottom dead centre. The firing intervals are equal at 180°, but the torque fluctuates because one power stroke is dying away as the next is building up. The distributor cam will have four lobes. The firing order will be 1, 3, 4, 2 or 1, 2, 4, 3.

Six cylinders
In line. The crankshaft torque may be increased by the use of six instead of four cylinders. Engines with this arrangement are longer, heavier, more complicated, and more expensive than the four-cylinder types, but they have much better balance, and can accelerate

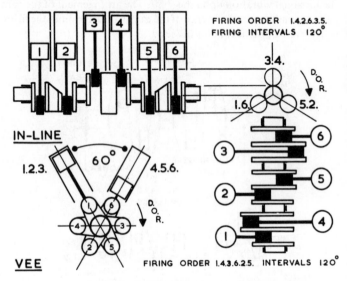

Fig. 3.2 Six-cylinder crankshafts: *above*, in-line; *below*, vee

much faster. They can also operate at lower speeds in top gear. The torque is also more even because the intervals between the power strokes are reduced to 120° and are equal. The shaft has six crankpins and either four or seven main journals. The crankpins are arranged in parallel pairs, the two centre pins being 120° from numbers 2 and 5 in one direction and 120° from numbers 1 and 6 in the opposite direction. The distributor cam will have six lobes and the firing order will be either 1, 5, 3, 6, 2, 4 or 1, 4, 2, 6, 3, 5.
Vee six. In this type two sets of three cylinders are staggered and arranged over the crankshaft to form a 60° vee. The shaft has six

crankpins arranged around it at 60° intervals. The firing intervals are 120° and the firing order is 1, 4, 2, 6, 3, 5.

Eight cylinders
In-line. These are sometimes also known as straight eights. They have more power, better acceleration, and a smoother torque than the six-cylinder types. Several different crankshaft arrangements can

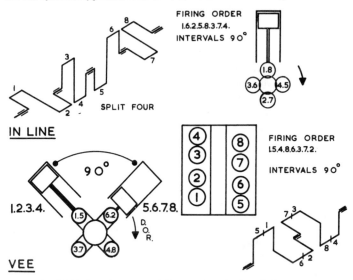

Fig. 3.3 Eight-cylinder crankshafts: *above*, in-line; *below*, vee

be used, each with about six alternative firing orders. In one arrangement the shaft resembles two flat-four crankshafts set end to end with their planes at right angles. The firing order most often used is 1, 5, 2, 6, 4, 8, 3, 7. An alternative crankshaft is more complicated, but is used because it avoids the longitudinal rocking of the engine. This is called the split-four shaft because it resembles a four-throw shaft cut in half and each half added to the ends of a second four-throw shaft turned through a right angle. The firing order is 1, 6, 2, 5, 8, 3, 7, 4. In both of these shaft arrangements the firing interval is 90°.

Although the in-line six- and eight-cylinder engines have a very smooth torque and are well balanced, they are rather long. Apart from the considerations of mass and room available, long engines suffer from the following technical difficulties:

(1) The length of the shaft makes it more liable to suffer from torsional vibration at normal running speeds.
(2) The length and shape of the inlet manifold make it almost impossible for the cylinders to induce the same mass of mixture, i.e. mixture distribution is poor.
(3) Because of the above, the overall mixture strength must be made excessively rich to avoid starvation of the weaker cylinders. This, combined with less efficient cooling of the cylinder heads, makes fuel consumption unnecessarily high.

To some extent these difficulties can be overcome by the use of torsional vibration dampers, and multi-carburettor or fuel injection systems, but these all add to the complication and expense of producing and maintaining the engine. For some or all of these reasons the straight eight has been replaced by the vee eight.

Vee eight. These are much shorter and have less mass than in-line types. Two banks of four cylinders are arranged at 90° above a three-bearing, four-throw crankshaft. The throws are 90° apart. Two connecting rods are attached to each crankpin, the big-ends rotating side by side. The left bank is numbered 1 to 4 and the right bank 5 to 8. Numbers 1 and 5 connecting rods are attached to number 1 crankpin, followed by 2 and 6, 3 and 1, and 4 and 8. The firing interval is 90° and the distributor has two four-lobed cams. The firing order is 1, 5, 4, 8, 6, 3, 7, 2.

Crankshaft vibration

When the crankshaft of an engine is rotating at high speed it is liable to vibrate with varying intensity. This vibration has two main causes. The first is the action upon the shaft of *unbalanced* forces, and the second is the *torsional* or twisting effect of the power strokes upon the shaft.

Out-of-balance forces

These are produced by any, or a combination of any, of the following:

(1) The fact that the crankshaft and flywheel assembly is not 'statically balanced'.

(2) The fact that the crankshaft and flywheel are not 'dynamically balanced'.

(3) The fact that the masses of the pistons and connecting rods are not balanced while in motion, i.e. the reciprocating masses are not balanced.

For balancing purposes the reciprocating masses are taken to be those of the piston, the gudgeon pin, and the upper third of the connecting rod. The rotating masses are taken to be those of the crankpin, the big-end, and the lower two-thirds of the connecting rod.

Static balance. In practice, the vibration of the crankshaft is reduced, as far as is economically possible, by the careful balancing of the crankshaft and flywheel. This may be done by fitting balance weights to the crankwebs, by removing metal from the crankwebs, or by arranging the crankpins on opposite sides of the shaft. When the main journals are supported by parallel and accurately levelled knife edges, the crankshaft should remain in any given position and have no tendency to rotate. Under these conditions the crankshaft is said to be statically balanced, i.e. balanced when stationary.

Dynamic balance. When the crankshaft of a multi-cylinder engine is rotating, it tends to rock from side to side, the motion being more violent at certain speeds. This is because the crankpins cannot be arranged exactly opposite each other and side thrusts are produced which act alternately in opposite directions. This rocking or pitching effect can be reduced by removing metal from certain parts of the crankwebs, the positions and masses of metal to be removed being found by the use of a special machine in which the crankshaft is rotated at various speeds. When this operation has been completed the crankshaft is said to be dynamically balanced, i.e. balanced while rotating.

Reciprocating mass balance. Both the static and dynamic balancing of the shaft are not too difficult to obtain because only simple rotating masses are involved. When the pistons and connecting rods are assembled to the crankpins, i.e. the reciprocating masses are added, the exact balancing of the complete assembly is a much more difficult task, and in some arrangements may even be impossible.

It is a feature of the crankshaft, piston and connecting-rod assembly that during the first half of the crankshaft revolution from top dead centre the piston moves down the cylinder at a greater speed than it does in the second half-revolution, due to the oblique angles of the connecting rod. The result of this is that the piston moves more than half its stroke in the first 90° of crankshaft rotation.

In a four-cylinder, in-line engine the two pistons which are moving down from top dead centre move faster than the two moving up to top dead centre, and the forces resulting from these movements do not counterbalance each other's effect upon the crankshaft. The result of this lack of balance is that the crankshaft is caused to vibrate in a direction parallel with the cylinders.

Torsional vibrations

The torque or turning motion of the crankshaft is derived from the power strokes, each of which forces a crankpin to rotate about the centre of the main journals and so tends to twist the shaft, i.e. subjects it to torsional stress. Although the power strokes may occur at equal angles of crankshaft rotation, the torque produced by them alternates between a high and a low value. The greater the number of power strokes which occur in each 720° of crankshaft rotation, the higher the average value of the torque and the more even the torque, i.e. the more powerful and even the torque.

The alternation of the torque and of the corresponding torsional loads may cause the shaft to vibrate about its own centre line. This vibration is sometimes referred to as shaft 'wind up', the shaft alternately winding up and releasing as it rotates.

In addition to the torsional vibration, the rotating shaft also has its own natural frequency or vibration. At certain speeds of rotation, known as critical speeds, the frequencies of these two vibrations may coincide and produce an excessive vibration called 'resonance'. The shaft vibration may then be so violent that the shaft will be fractured.

If the crankshaft is long, and also if the crankwebs are very heavy, the frequency of the resonance vibrations will occur within the normal speed range of the crankshaft. This must be avoided by careful attention to the design of the crankshaft assembly, and by the fitting of a suitable torsional vibration damper.

The crankshaft damper

Several different designs of crankshaft torsional vibration damper are in use but they operate in such a way as to allow the crankshaft to offer a greater resistance to torsional loads. This has the effect of increasing the natural frequency of the shaft so that resonance vibration can only occur at speeds beyond those normal for the shaft. The damper is a small flywheel which normally rotates with the crankshaft but which can also rotate in relation to the shaft when torque variations occur.

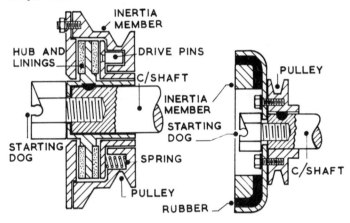

Fig. 3.4 Types of damper: *left*, CV or friction; *right*, bonded rubber

Construction

One type of damper consists of a hub which is keyed to the forward end of the crankshaft and so always rotates with it. A heavy metal disc, known as the inertia member, is so arranged that it will only rotate with the hub when the hub itself is rotating under an even torque, i.e. at a constant velocity. The inertia member is usually friction driven by the hub through spring-loaded friction linings, or through a thick fluid, or through a bonded rubber ring or pads.

Operation

When the frequencies of the torsional vibrations from the power stroke coincide with the natural frequencies of the crankshaft, to produce dangerous resonance frequencies, the crankshaft vibrates about its own centre line – or winds up and releases. This results in the damper hub accelerating and slowing down as it rotates. Because of its large mass, the inertia member cannot quickly follow these velocity changes and it therefore continues to rotate smoothly. In so doing, it overcomes the friction between itself and the hub and absorbs the energy of the resonance vibration, so bringing the frequency of these vibrations below the level which may result in damage to the crankshaft.

The fan-belt drive pulley is often combined with the damper, and this results in a much smoother transmission of torque to the water pump and dynamo. Use of the damper reduces the chance of crankshaft failure or distortion, and also provides a smoother torque at the camshaft.

NOTE. It is important to note that these units are designed to operate with one particular design of crankshaft assembly. They are not interchangeable between different crankshaft designs and are not adjustable except where the engine manufacturer issues detailed procedure, together with details of the loadings to be used.

THE MAIN BEARINGS

The crankshaft is supported in the crankcase by three, five or seven main bearings in which the main journals rotate. The bearings may be thick walled or thin walled and are split, plain types.

Thick-wall type
Each bearing consists of a pair of phosphor-bronze backs or shells which are lined to a thickness of about three millimetres with white metal. When used with steel, this metal has a very low frictional resistance. The white metal consists of about 88 % tin, 4 % copper and 8 % antimony, and has a low melting-point. Should the lubrication of the bearing fail, the resulting temperature rise of the bearing and journal will melt the white metal and the noise that results will warn the driver to stop – so reducing the chance of damaging the crankshaft. These bearings are machined to size and given a good finish but generally require hand scraping to obtain the correct bedding-in after fitting to the crankcase webs. The big-end bearings of the connecting rods are similar in this respect.

This type of bearing was quite successful for many years, but as bearing loads and running speeds have increased, and are still being increased, these bearings have been replaced by the thin-wall types. This is because the white metal tends to be beaten out by the shock loads, so breaking up the surface and causing the bearing to fail long before it is worn out. A further point is that the thin-wall bearings are much simpler and cheaper to replace.

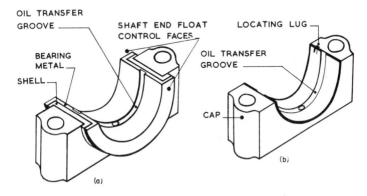

Fig. 3.5 Main bearings: (a) thick wall; (b) thin wall

Thin-wall type

These bearings consist of a pair of thin steel shells lined to a depth of about 0·13 mm with white metal. The shallow depth of the anti-friction metal improves the fatigue resistance of the bearings and these types are said to have four times the life of the thick-wall bearings. The shells are formed very accurately and have very fine surface finishes. No hand fitting work is required and none should ever be attempted. The bearings must be properly fitted into their recesses and located by the small lugs or projections pressed from the steel backs. These prevent the shells from being turned or moved along the journal during installation. It is most important that both the backs of the shells and their recesses in the webs and bearing caps be perfectly clean when fitting the shells, as only friction prevents their rotation in service. (Interference fit under correct torque load.)

Many bearings now in use are lined with lead-bronze. This metal is much harder, and stronger in compression, than white metal and, although it is more expensive, it has about three times as long a life when used in these bearings. Sometimes only the half bearing under the greater load is lined with lead-bronze, the other half being lined with white metal, i.e. the lower half of the main bearing and the upper half of the big-end bearing are lead-bronze. This is to both save expense and reduce the total friction in the bearing, lead-bronze having more frictional resistance than white metal. Lead-bronze consists of about 70 % copper, 28 % lead and 2 % tin.

Another metal used for heavy-duty bearings is copper-lead. This contains more lead and less copper than the lead-bronze, together with a small percentage of tin or silver, and is a softer metal.

White metal is used for the main and big-end bearings of most petrol engines, copper-lead being used for the more expensive high-performance engines. Lead-bronze is used in the compression-ignition engines where bearing pressures are higher and more sustained. The best combination of materials for long-life bearings is a hardened steel shaft in a lead-bronze shell which has been coated with a thin film of lead and indium, the film preventing corrosion and reducing scoring of the journal.

Clearances
The running clearance between the main journals and their bearings is about 0·02 mm for each 25 mm of bearing diameter. Because of their higher frictional resistance, the harder bearing metals require slightly larger clearances to reduce the chance of seizure to the journals when the journals expand under heat.

The end float of the crankshaft in the crankcase must be limited to between 0·1 mm and 0·25 mm. End float is controlled by thrust faces on both sides of the centre main bearing or by a similar arrangement at the rear main bearing.

Torque loading
The main bearing caps must be tightened down correctly to avoid distortion of the bearings or looseness of the shells, either of which will result in bearing failure. The nuts must be tightened by means of a torque wrench, the loadings being between 54 N m and 270 N m.

NOTE. Always refer to the manufacturers' manuals for fitting instruction. Never guess, or rely on memory.

Function
The connecting rod is used to transfer thrust in either direction between the piston and the crankpin.

Construction
The connecting rod is usually about twice as long as the stroke of the engine and is subjected to forces which try to bend, stretch, and compress it. It is usually of H-shaped cross-section to resist

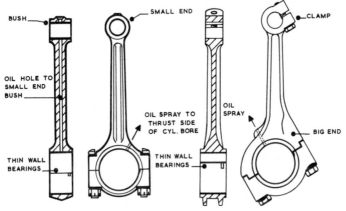

Fig. 3.6 Connecting rods

these forces and is either an alloy-steel forging, or an aluminium-alloy forging of equivalent strength but lighter in weight. The small end of the rod carries the gudgeon pin in either a phosphor-bronze bush or in a clamped eye.

The large, or big-end, bearing is split to allow it to be fitted to the crankpin, thin-wall white metal or copper-lead bearing shells being used. In some engines the split of the bearing is oblique, to make the withdrawal of the rod up the cylinder bore possible. Clearances are about the same as for the main bearings.

The lubrication of the big-end bearing is very important and is usually arranged by feeding high-pressure oil, through a duct or drilling in the crankshaft, from a main journal to the crankpin. In some connecting rods a small hole is drilled through the upper shell and rod so that it lines up with the main feed hole of the crankpin once each revolution. This results in a small jet of oil being sprayed out to lubricate the cylinder wall. It is most important that this hole, where used, be fitted towards the thrust side of the cylinder. The correct torque loadings must be used when tightening down the nuts of the bearing cap.

CRANKCASE OIL SEALING

Because the ends of the crankshaft pass through the front and rear walls of the crankcase, and the main bearings here are supplied by oil under high pressure, it is necessary to use some form of oil sealing to prevent oil leakage from the engine.

At the forward end of the crankshaft a felt ring is often fitted into

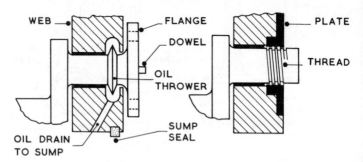

Fig. 3.7 Crankshaft oil sealing

the timing case to fit closely around the crankshaft pulley. An alternative method is sometimes used where the timing case is made in two parts, the felt ring being replaced by two semicircular strips of graphite-impregnated wick materials. Spring-loaded seals are also used. In all arrangements most of the oil escaping from the bearing is prevented from reaching the seal itself by an oil thrower ring. This is a saucer-shaped steel disc with a sharp edge; as oil reaches it the oil is thrown from the disc and shaft, to fall back into the sump.

At the rear end of the crankshaft the oil must be prevented from entering the clutch housing. One method is to use an oil-thrower ring which in this case is part of the crankshaft, being a knife-edged circular projection positioned outside the bearing. Oil thrown from the knife edge is returned to the sump through a pipe or duct in the bearing cap. An alternative method is to machine a shallow square thread half in the shaft end and half in a special cylindrical housing fitting closely over the shaft and accurately centralized. Oil escaping from the bearing is wound back into it again or is forced back to a drain into the sump. Sometimes combinations of these methods are used.

THE FLYWHEEL

Function

The main function of the flywheel is to retain some of the energy given to the crankshaft during the power stroke and then to release this energy to keep the crankshaft turning during the idle strokes, i.e. the flywheel helps to keep the crankshaft rotating smoothly. The flywheel also forms one driving face of the clutch assembly and acts as a gear for the engagement of the starter motor.

Construction

The flywheel consists of a steel or cast-iron disc with a very heavy rim. This mass, at the largest possible radius, gives the flywheel a large moment of inertia, i.e. resistance to changes in velocity, which enable it to store and release energy as required. The greater the number of power strokes during each crankshaft revolution the lighter the flywheel can be, and the quicker the response of the engine to the demanded changes in speed.

The rear face of the flywheel is used to mount the clutch assembly, and this face is usually hardened to resist wear. The outer circumference of the flywheel carries a set or ring of gear teeth which may be integral with the flywheel or may be a shrink fit. The gear on the end of the shaft of the starter motor engages with this ring gear when the motor is energized.

It is essential to the balance of the crankshaft and flywheel assembly that both should rotate about the same axis. The flywheel is therefore usually recessed to fit tightly over a forged flange at the end of the crankshaft, and is held in position by two dowels. The flywheel is secured to the crankshaft by a set of bolts which must be

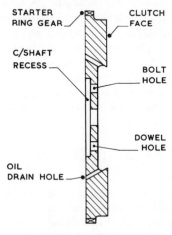

STARTER RING GEAR

CLUTCH FACE

C/SHAFT RECESS

BOLT HOLE

DOWEL HOLE

OIL DRAIN HOLE

Fig. 3.8 Flywheel

tightened down to the correct torque loading and locked by wire or lock plates. If the flywheel circumference is marked to assist in valve or ignition timing operations, either the dowels or the bolts may be so arranged that it is impossible to mount the flywheel in the wrong position.

THE POPPET VALVE

Function

The valve is used to control the flow of gases into and out of the cylinders and combustion chambers. Usually there is one inlet valve and one exhaust valve but engines with two valves of each type have been used.

Operating conditions

Inlet valve. The inlet valve is kept relatively cool by the mixture which flows around it as each fresh charge is induced, and normally operates at about 250 °C.

Exhaust valve. For very short periods the exhaust valve is subjected to temperatures of over 2000 °C but it normally operates at about 750 °C, i.e. at red heat.

Both valves. Both valves must make a good gas-tight seal against pressures of about 4200 kN/m² at the above temperatures. They must also resist corrosion and scaling. As they are held down to their seats by strong springs they must also resist being stretched, and must not be distorted by the continual hammering of their heads upon their seats.

Materials

These are usually high-tensile alloy steels, a different alloy being used for the exhaust valves. Although both may be of the same dimension, an inlet must never be used to replace an exhaust valve, or failure will result. In some modern engines the valves cannot be interchanged by mistake as the inlet valves have much larger head diameters. The steels used for inlet valves are usually those containing the alloys nickel, chromium, and molybdenum.

Steels for exhaust valves include those with the alloys cobalt chromium and silicon chromium, and nickel-chromium austenitic steel, all of which resist oxidation and corrosion and wear.

Construction

The poppet valve consists of a single piece of alloy steel forged into a shape somewhat resembling that of a mushroom. The valve head is usually flat on top while its underside is accurately ground to an angle of either 45° or 30°. This machined surface is known as the face of the valve and between the face and the top of the head, at 90° to the top, is the margin or land. This thickness of metal is used to prevent the burning of the edge of the head. The cylindrical portion of the valve under the head is known as the stem and this terminates in the tip. Valve tips are often made very hard, or are separate hardened pieces permanently attached to the stem. Just before the tip is a groove in which collets of the valve's spring retainer cap are fitted.

Valve assembly

The valve stem is supported by a cylindrical sleeve known as the valve guide. Guides are usually made from a close-grained, chilled cast iron which is very hard and brittle, but some are being made from a very highly-compressed iron powder. These have a very long service life because they are hard wearing; this material retains relatively large quantities of lubricating oil. Guides for cylinder heads

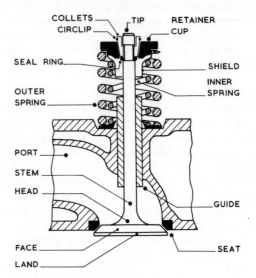

Fig. 3.9 Poppet valve assembly

Fig. 3.10 Head shapes

of aluminium alloy may be of aluminium bronze. All of these guides are either shrink or interference fits in their bores. The clearance between the valve stem and the guide should not normally exceed 0·05 mm. If the valve can be rocked sideways in the guide when both are dry, either or both are worn beyond permissible limits and should be replaced.

The valve is held closed down to its seat by the action of one or two coil springs. When two are used, one is fitted inside the other, and is wound in the opposite direction to reduce the chance of

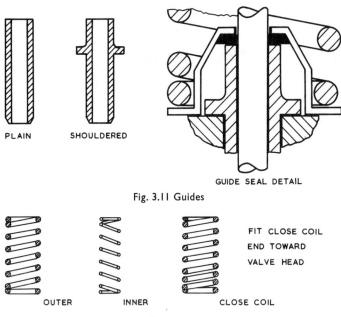

PLAIN   SHOULDERED

GUIDE SEAL DETAIL

Fig. 3.11 Guides

OUTER   INNER   CLOSE COIL

FIT CLOSE COIL
END TOWARD
VALVE HEAD

Fig. 3.12 Springs

fouling should either spring fracture. The advantages of the double spring arrangement are that:

(a) Valve bounce and power loss at high speeds is reduced.

(b) The springs have a longer life because their load is shared.

(c) The valve is subjected to less side thrust as it is moved in its guide.

The springs enclose the valve, one end of the spring being located on the cylinder head or block casting and the other by the spring retainer cup. This is attached to the valve stem by two collets. These are small steel parts which fit into a groove in the valve stem and when so fitted their outer surfaces form a conical wedge. The wedge is enclosed by a tapered hole in the spring retainer cup, the spring force locking the collets tight into the stem groove.

In some engines the collets and cup are combined, and in overhead valve arrangements the collets may be fitted with a safety device. This takes the form of a spring clip which is fitted into a groove in the collets – so preventing the valve falling into the cylinder if the spring should break.

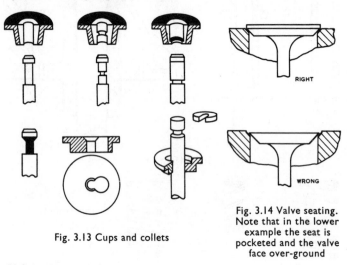

Fig. 3.13 Cups and collets

Fig. 3.14 Valve seating. Note that in the lower example the seat is pocketed and the valve face over-ground

Valve seats

The valve seat may be machined from the cast iron of the cylinder head or block. Many of these seats are now coated with a nickel-chromium alloy called 'Stellite'. This is applied by a gas welding process and provides a very hard-wearing surface. When refacing becomes necessary special grinding stones must be used.

Inserted seats may also be used and these, because harder wearing materials can be used, have a much longer service life than the plain cast-iron seats. These inserts must have the same coefficient of expansion as the material of the cylinder head or block into which they are fitted, e.g. a high nickel-chrome alloy steel for cast iron or nickel-chrome-manganese alloy steel for aluminium alloy.

Inserts may be screwed or shrunk into position, or be an interference fit. As an alternative to heating the block or head the inserts may be chilled by immersion in liquid oxygen or dry ice – expanding to become a very secure fit as they return to air temperature.

Valve face and seat angles are either 30° or 45°. The 45° seat is a good all-round one for general service, but inlet valves may be cut at 30° to provide a quicker opening of the port for the same amount of valve lift. Inlet valves and ports may be larger to permit easier and quicker charging of the cylinders. The 30° valves and seats may require servicing at slightly more frequent intervals.

THE CAMSHAFT

Function

The camshaft is used to locate, support, and rotate the cams in such a way that each valve is opened at the correct time, is held open for the correct time, and is closed at the correct time in relation to the movement of the pistons.

Construction

The inlet and exhaust valve cams for each cylinder are paired and their relative positions on the shaft are such that they form an angle when viewed from the end of the shaft. This angle determines the opening and closing times of the valves, while the shape of the cam determines how long each valve is held open. Each pair of cams therefore determine the valve timing of their cylinder.

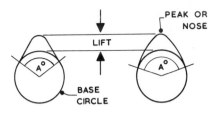

Fig. 3.15 Cams (A° = valve-open period)

The correct induction sequence (firing order) is obtained by the disposition or arrangement of the pairs of cams around the shaft, i.e. by arranging the pairs at the correct angles to each other.

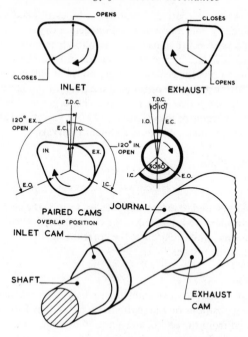

Fig. 3.16 Cam pair

The camshaft is a one-piece forging of tough alloy steel, or a casting of alloy iron similar to that used for cast-iron crankshafts. In some compression-ignition engines the cam pairs are made separately and then secured to the shaft. The shaft must be stiff and usually has three or four journals. These must be of greater diameter than the sweep of the cams to enable the camshaft to pass through the journal bearings in the crankcase webs and walls. In addition to the cams and journals, the camshaft may also have an eccentric to operate the mechanical petrol pump, and a skew gear to drive the lubricating oil pump and the distributor unit of the ignition system. All the wearing surfaces must be hardened, but the shaft itself must be tough to resist shock and torsion loads. Although the valves themselves may only weigh a few grams a force of over 1300 N may be required to operate each one at very high speeds.

Position

The camshaft is generally arranged above, to one side of, and parallel with the crankshaft, and rotates in bearings in the cylinder block. These bearings may be plain holes bored in the cylinder block or crankcase walls and webs, or white metal bushes. The clearance between the journals and the bushes is between 0·025 mm and 0·075 mm and they are lubricated by high-pressure oil through ducts in the crankcase webs which connect to the main oil gallery pipe. The longitudinal movement (end float) of the shaft is limited to between 0·075 mm and 0·15 mm by means of a shimmed thrust plate which fits into a groove machined in the forward end of the front journal of the shaft.

Other arrangements are also used, but the important thing is that float of the shaft end must be limited in both directions. The front journal is also used to support and locate the camshaft driving gear or chain wheel.

In some high-performance engines the camshaft may be arranged very high up in the cylinder block or on top of the cylinder head. Single camshafts are usually arranged at the near side of the engine. Two camshafts may be used and these may have both inlet and exhaust cams or one shaft may carry all the inlet cams while the second carries all the exhaust cams.

Wherever the camshaft is mounted it must be driven from the crankshaft. When the engine is operating under the four-stroke

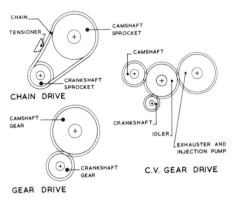

Fig. 3.17 Camshaft drives (low)

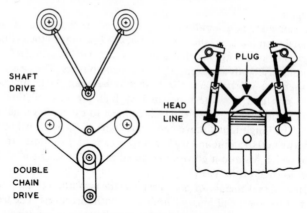

SHAFT
DRIVE

DOUBLE
CHAIN
DRIVE

PLUG

HEAD
LINE

Fig. 3.18 Camshaft drives (high)

cycle the camshaft is driven at half the speed of the crankshaft –
because each valve is required to operate only once in two
revolutions of the crankshaft. This speed reduction is obtained by
having twice the number of teeth on the driving gear of the
camshaft than there are on the crankshaft gear. Both gears are
keyed to their respective shafts. Camshafts may be driven by one
or more chains, by trains of gears, or by a system of gear-driven
shafts.

OVERHEAD VALVE GEAR

Push rod operated
In these arrangements the valves are inverted and are mounted in
the cylinder head. The spring and guide arrangement is similar to
that used in the side-valve types but the cam followers or tappets
are usually hollow and have no adjusting screws. A push rod and a
rocker arm are fitted between the tappet and the valve in such a
way that the lifting of the tappet causes the valve to be forced down,
away from its seat.

The tappet clearance, or valve clearance, is arranged between the
valve tip and the rocker arm tip, while the adjusting screw and
locknut are fitted to the other side of the rocker arm. The end of the
adjusting screw is a hardened steel ball which is fitted into a steel

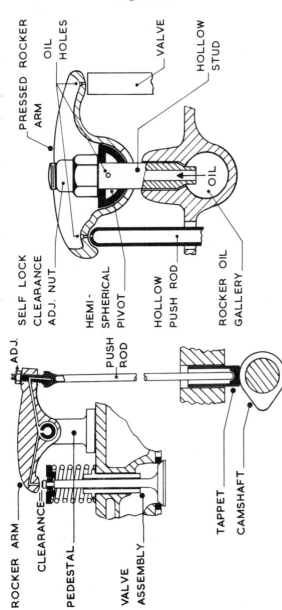

Fig. 3.19 Push-rod valve operation

Fig. 3.20 Alternative rocker-arm assembly

ROCKER ARM

CLEARANCE

PEDESTAL

VALVE ASSEMBLY

ADJ.

PUSH ROD

TAPPET

CAMSHAFT

PRESSED ROCKER ARM

OIL HOLES

VALVE

HOLLOW STUD

SELF LOCK CLEARANCE ADJ. NUT

HEMI-SPHERICAL PIVOT

HOLLOW PUSH ROD

ROCKER OIL GALLERY

OIL

cup formed in the upper end of the push rod. The push rod may be solid or hollow steel with a hardened, spherical lower end.

The shaft which carries the rocker arms is usually hollow, and is fed by lubricating oil under pressure. The rocker arms may be steel forgings or impacted, powdered-iron, diecastings. Pressed steel types are also used. Phosphor-bronze bushes may be fitted. These are lubricated through holes drilled in the rocker shaft. Many rocker arms are also drilled in such a way that the lubricating oil can be forced through them to lubricate the adjusting screw ball end and the valve tip. The valve and guide are lubricated by the oil splashed from the pressure-fed areas. In overhead-valve engines, a high oil consumption may be caused by oil mist being drawn down the inlet valve guides during the induction strokes. This may be reduced by the fitting of felt or rubber washers around the valve stems.

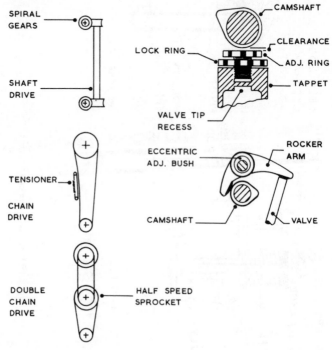

Fig. 3.21 Camshaft drives (overhead)

Overhead camshaft

In these designs the valves are arranged in one straight line, with the camshaft immediately above them. As push rods and rocker arms are not needed, the number of moving parts is reduced. In some designs the tappets and their adjusting devices enclose the valves and double valve springs are used. The camshaft is driven from the crankshaft by a vertical shaft, spiral bevel gears being fitted at each end. Overhead camshaft designs are usually quieter in operation, easier to lubricate, and are more efficient than the push-rod designs

Where the valves are arranged in more than one line, twin camshafts are employed. These may be mounted on the cylinder head or high up in the cylinder block. In the latter arrangement push rods and rocker arms are employed. The camshafts are usually chain driven and more than one chain may be used.

In a few engines the inlet valves are of overhead design and push-rod operated, while the exhaust valves are side by side. Both are operated from a single camshaft.

Although all of these arrangements are more complicated and expensive to produce and service than the more common arrangements, this extra cost is justified by their superior performance and

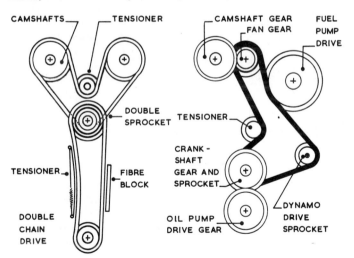

Fig. 3.22 *left*, Twin camshaft drive; *right*, CV engine drives

economy in operation. This results mainly from the fact that they permit the use of special shapes of combustion chamber which produce more power from a given weight of fuel, usually by permitting the use of higher compression ratios without detonation taking place.

Timing diagrams

These are used to illustrate the timing of the valves, and are usually to be found in the workshop manuals. They show the direction of

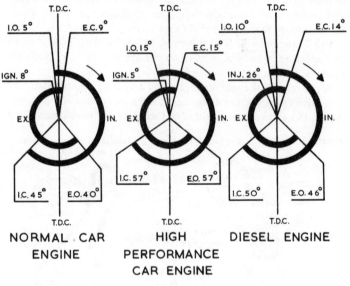

NORMAL CAR ENGINE   HIGH PERFORMANCE CAR ENGINE   DIESEL ENGINE

Fig. 3.23 Timing diagrams

rotation of the crankshaft and the points at which the valves are opened and closed. The valve-open periods are usually heavily marked. Note that two complete crankshaft revolutions are made in four-stroke engine timing diagrams and that the overlap is larger in very high-speed engines.

When studying timing diagrams note that two complete crankshaft revolutions are made in four-stroke engines and that the over-lap is greater in high-speed engines.

Timing operations
The shapes of the cams will provide the correct movement of the valves, and their arrangement around the camshaft will provide their correct operating sequence, but these movements must be accurately related to the movements of the pistons. The relating of camshaft to crankshaft rotation is called the timing of the valves and it consists of three basic operations:
(1) Positioning the crankshaft.
(2) Positioning the camshaft.
(3) Connecting the two together.

In many engines the timing gears or sprockets can only be attached to their shafts in one way. These gears are usually marked and the timing operation consists only of aligning the marks in accordance with the makers' instructions.

A rule-of-thumb method which can be used to time most engines of older design makes use of the valve overlap period to determine the correct camshaft position. The tappet clearances are set correctly and the disconnected camshaft is rotated by hand until in one pair of valves both are rocking open, i.e. the overlap position is reached. The crankshaft is then rotated until the piston of that cylinder is at top dead centre. This is usually when the crankshaft pulley key is at top dead centre or bottom dead centre. The two shafts are then connected by the gears or chains, the pitch of the teeth usually being so large that an error is obvious. The timing of all the other cylinders must be correct due to the construction of the two shafts. Timing can be done on any cylinder, but it is usual to time on number one.

In modern high-performance engines the overlap is greater, and a more complicated and accurate method must be used. In some engines the opening or closing position of one valve is marked on the flywheel. The correct position of the crankshaft is therefore easy to obtain. The correct position of the camshaft is obtained by means of a dial gauge mounted over the particular valve. The camshaft is rotated until the gauge indicates that the valve is either on the point of opening or closing and the camshaft is stopped at that exact position. The two shafts are then connected by the gears or chains.

In some engines the chain sprocket can be fitted in slightly different positions on the camshaft to assist in obtaining the exact timing.

Timing chains have a tendency to stretch during a period of operation and so become noisy. The resulting slackness also reduces the accuracy of the original valve timing and many engines

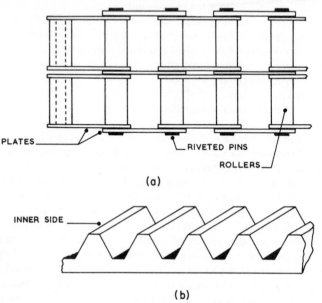

PLATES

RIVETED PINS

ROLLERS

(a)

INNER SIDE

(b)

Fig. 3.24 Drives: (a) chain detail; (b) notched belt detail

are fitted with automatic chain tensioners. These require readjustment or replacement only at long intervals. The tensioners may consist of a spring-loaded steel strip which presses on the slack side of the chain, or a spring-loaded sprocket. Long chains must always have automatic tensioners fitted. Where split links are used in the chain, the closed end of the link retainer must face the direction in which the chain runs. Some chains have bright links which are fitted into marked teeth on the sprockets to make valve timing easier and quicker.

Gears tend to be more noisy than chains unless they are made from a special material. They also become more noisy as their teeth, and the main bearings of the crankshaft, wear. Gears and chains are usually both lubricated by a small spray of high-pressure oil supplied from the duct of the forward crankcase web.

Valve clearances

These are sometimes called tappet clearances and their correct size is important to the efficient operation of the engine. In side valve arrangements this clearance is made between the tip of the valve and the tappet or tappet-adjusting screw. In overhead valve arrangements the clearance is made between the tip of the valve and the foot of the rocker arm, or between the tip of the valve and a special form of tappet used in overhead camshaft engines.

The valve clearance is given to make sure that the valve is fully closed by its springs under all operating temperatures, i.e. in spite of the different effects of temperature on the valve, cylinder head, and cylinder block. The clearance is set with the help of feeler gauges and varies between different engines. It may also vary between inlet and exhaust valves in the same engine.

Valve clearances must be adjusted under the conditions specified by the engine manufacturer, i.e. when the engine is hot or cold. Excessive clearances will result in the engine being noisy and, more important, extra wear will occur, and a loss of power will result from a reduced valve-open period, i.e. the valves will open later and close earlier. If the clearances are too small, the valve will not be fully closed and over a period of operation the valve and seat faces will be burned. Compression and power will be reduced by the extension of the valve-open period permitting the gases to escape.

Clearance setting

When adjusting clearances it is very important to make sure that the tappet is on the back of its cam, i.e. that the cam is not lifting the tappet. Possibly the easiest way of obtaining the position for tappet and cam is to work to a sequence; one such method is to add one to the total number of valves, e.g. a total of nine for a four-cylinder engine.

If the clearance of number one valve is to be set, the crankshaft is rotated until number eight valve is fully open. At this point, number one tappet is on the back of its cam and its clearance can be set correctly. If number two is next, the crankshaft is rotated until number seven valve is fully opened, when the clearance of number two can be set. The sequence is repeated, the numbers of the valve clearance being set and the valve being opened always adding up to nine. The full sequence is given below.

Adjust number 1 clearance when number 8 valve is fully open.
Adjust number 2 clearance when number 7 valve is fully open.
Adjust number 3 clearance when number 6 valve is fully open.
Adjust number 4 clearance when number 5 valve is fully open.
Adjust number 5 clearance when number 4 valve is fully open.
Adjust number 6 clearance when number 3 valve is fully open.
Adjust number 7 clearance when number 2 valve is fully open.
Adjust number 8 clearance when number 1 valve is fully open.

As the cams of each pair selected in this method are 180° apart on the camshaft the mechanic can always be sure that the tappet of the valve on which he is working is on the back of its cam.

4   Lubrication

This is the name given to materials applied between moving surfaces to reduce friction, heat, and wear.

Oils

Each of the many different oils used in units of the vehicle is specially compounded to make it the best possible lubricant under the operating conditions of that unit. The correct lubricant for a particular unit cannot be determined by its appearance or by its feel. It must only be used after a series of physical and chemical tests have proved that it will provide adequate lubrication under all the different combinations of load, speed, and temperature involved in the operation of the unit.

Oil properties

These are the characteristics of the oil which make it suitable for a particular purpose. Two of the more important of these are 'body' and 'flow'.

Body. This is the name given to the ability of the oil to maintain an unbroken film of oil between two surfaces under all normal conditions of speed and load. Body is sometimes called oiliness; it is the oil's resistance to being squeezed out by high pressures. Body may be required to maintain the oil film under pressures as high as $14\,000\,kN/m^2$. It also acts to cushion the surfaces against shock load.

Flow. Flow is the ability of the oil to spread easily over the surfaces, and to pass easily through small holes and clearances. Flow is affected by temperature, being reduced as the temperature is reduced and vice versa. Flow and body are opposed properties and the correct balance between them must be obtained for each particular purpose.

Viscosity. This is the measure of the *rate* of flow. An oil which flows quickly has a low viscosity (it is thin) and vice versa. The viscosity decreases with temperature increase, and the effect of temperature upon an oil must be considered.

Viscosity index. This is the number given to an oil to indicate the degree of *change* in its viscosity as the temperature changes. A low index means that the viscosity of the oil varies greatly between high and low temperatures. A high-quality oil would have a viscosity index of between 90 and 100.

Viscosity measurement. Viscosity is measured by the use of the Redwood viscometer, and the measurements taken enable us to compare oils on a basis of viscosity. In this apparatus a quantity of oil is held in a container surrounded by a water jacket. An orifice is fitted in the base of the container and is sealed by a steel ball. The water in the jacket is heated until a steady temperature of 21 °C is obtained. The ball is then lifted clear of the orifice, which has an area of 1 square mm, and the time measured in seconds for exactly 50 cm³ (or 50 ml) to pass through the orifice. The procedure is repeated at 60 °C and 99 °C. The time in Redwood seconds at these temperatures provides the basis for comparisons between different oils.

SAE numbers

These were established by the American Society of Automotive Engineers in order to classify oils by their viscosity. Each number defines, within specified limits, the viscosity of the oil at a given temperature. SAE numbers in no way refer to the quality or any special properties of the oil. The older English grades are now replaced by the SAE system.

SAE	English	SAE	English
10	Extra light	40	Medium heavy
20	Light	50	Heavy
30	Medium	60	Extra heavy

The viscosities of the thin and thick lubricating oils most frequently used were established as the lower and upper limits for the SAE scales. The scale was then divided into five grades, each of which was given a number which covered a range of viscosities at 99 °C. Engine-oil numbers are given in the table; transmission oils are SAE 75, 80, 90, 140, and 250.

W numbers

A further range of SAE grades and numbers has since been established to cover the effect of *low* temperatures upon viscosity. Some oils thicken more than others at low temperatures and, although they may be within the same grading limits at higher temperatures, they may cause starting difficulties at low temperatures, e.g. two oils may both be in the SAE 20 grading at 99 °C but one may have a much higher viscosity than the other at −18 °C.

Each of these grades has a specified range of viscosity at − 18 °C but is also within acceptable minimum limits at 99 °C to afford protection against excessive thinning at the higher temperatures. The letter W is an indication of these grades and the numbers are 5W, 10W, and 20W. Some good-quality oils may be able to meet the grading requirements at both temperatures and this is indicated by using both numbers, e.g. 20/20W.

Multigrade oils

These are oils containing an additive which reduces the effect of temperature on their viscosity, i.e. they thicken less when cold and thin less when hot. Multigrade oils make starting easier by reducing oil drag, circulate more easily under all conditions, and still provide adequate lubrication when hot. Such oils may be graded as 10W/30 – which means that the oil comes within the SAE viscosity grading of 10 at −18 °C, and under 30 grading at 99 °C.

TRANSMISSION LUBRICATION

Modern gear assemblies have to have as little weight and volume as possible. Small gears are therefore subjected to both high torques and speeds, and the gear teeth are subjected to high contact pressures and have only small clearances.

The main requirements of a transmission oil are:
(1) The ability to maintain, in spite of high contact pressures, an unbroken film of oil at the contact areas of the teeth and bearings.
(2) Sufficient viscosity to resist being squeezed out but not so much as to result in channelling.
(3) The ability to act as an efficient coolant.

Transmission oils contain additives to make them more suited to their conditions of operation. A small quantity of chlorine may be added to reduce wear, sulphur to reduce 'scuffing', and molybdenum disulphide to reduce friction and wear. Another additive may be used to reduce oxidation. Gear assemblies are usually splash lubricated, the movements of the gears circulating oil to all parts of the unit. Epicyclic gearboxes, overdrives, and automatic transmissions are pressure fed by their own pumps. Gear cases may be made from aluminium alloy to dissipate the heat more efficiently.

Gearbox oils
(a) Sliding mesh. SAE 140 or SAE 140 E.P.
(b) Synchro mesh. Cars: SAE 40/50 engine oil: Commercial vehicles SAE 90.
(c) Epicyclic. A low viscosity oil SAE 30/40 or a special oil.
(d) Automatic. Only the recommended oil.

Rear-axle oils
(a) Spiral bevel. Cars: SAE 90. Commercial vehicles: SAE 140.
(b) Hypoid. An extreme-pressure oil with a special additive which comes into action due to the heat produced at a point in danger of local seizure. It reacts with the heated surface to form a protective film which reduces metal-to-metal contact. Hypoid axles use SAE 70 to SAE 140 EP oils.
(c) Worm. Worms have a very high contact pressure combined with a sliding motion. Much heat is produced and a special oil containing sulphur, chlorine, and phosphorus is required.

Oil changes
The manufacturers' instructions should be carried out, but usually gearbox and rear axle oils should be changed at 8000 to 10 000 km intervals.

GREASES

These are compounds formed by adding metallic soaps and thickeners to lubricating oil. Additives may also be used to provide extra properties such as resistance to spread under impact loads or in the presence of water. The compounding is done under pressure and at temperatures suited to the type of grease, i.e. grease with a high melting-point is made at a higher temperature than soft grease.

Chassis grease
This must resist being squeezed out of bearings by shock loads and high pressures, and it must not be washed out by water. It is a soft and tenacious grease with a lithium or lime-soda base, and is applied at regular intervals by a grease gun. In some vehicles it may be replaced by an SAE 140 oil; in heavier commercial vehicles a grease with a higher proportion of lime-soda is required.

White oxide grease
This is used for brake shoe pivots, adjusters, and some expander tappets. It may also be used for some water-pump bearings. It is a high-melting-point grease with the addition of white zinc oxide, and it repels water. The melting-point is about 300 °C.

High-melting-point grease
This is a soft grease which melts at about 350 °C. It is used for wheel and other bearings of the ball or roller type. It must be able to resist high pressures and it must not 'channel'. Channelling is a serious fault in which the grease is pushed out of the way of a ball (or roller or gear tooth) and fails to lubricate the path of the next ball because it is too thick to flow back into place. The parts then run under dry friction conditions and wear and heat cause rapid failure. The heat and the high contact pressures combine to weld together very minute high spots on the surfaces. These welds are broken and re-formed, and the surfaces are very quickly destroyed – they may then weld or seize completely.

Water-pump grease
This is a soft grease which is water repellent and heat resistant. It may contain colloidal graphite.

Special greases
These have been developed for special conditions:
(1) Rubber grease for the sealing cups of fluid brakes and clutch cylinders. This is used both as a lubricant for the cups when first fitted and to protect them from contamination by other oils and greases during their installation.
(2) A grease with a very high melting-point for wheel bearings where disc brakes are fitted.

(3) A high-melting-point grease containing molybdenum disulphide to further reduce friction.
(4) A silicone compound for waterproofing ignition cables, chromium-plated parts, and rubber mouldings.

ENGINE LUBRICATION

Sliding, rotary, and reciprocating motions all occur in the operation of the engine and these motions are opposed by the various forms of friction. The use of the correct lubricant is vital to the efficient operation and long life of the engine.

Operating conditions

The selection of an oil suitable for use in a particular engine depends upon:
(a) The forms of motion and the types of friction involved in the operation of the engine.
(b) The magnitude of the forces and pressures acting upon the different surfaces.
(c) The range of operating temperatures.
(d) The speeds of the various forms of motion.

In the petrol engine the temperature of the exhaust valves may exceed 600 °C (red heat), while the piston crown temperature may be between 200 °C and 300 °C. The pressure acting upon the piston crown at the start of the power stroke is between 3100 kN/m^2 and 4100 kN/m^2 and this results in bearing pressures of up to 14000 kN/m^2 being applied to the main and big-end bearings. The crankshaft may rotate at up to 6000 rev/min. Under these conditions the temperature of the lubricating oil is usually between 50 °C and 100 °C.

In the diesel or compression-ignition engine the temperatures and speeds are lower, but the pressures are higher and are more sustained.

Modern car engines generally use an SAE 20/20W oil all the year round, or a multigrade 10W/30. Alternatively they may use an SAE 20/20W for the winter and SAE 30 for the summer. Worn engines may require a thicker oil such as SAE 40 or SAE 50.

Modern oils all contain additives which reduce the speed of the oil breakdown. One of these additives reduces oxidation. A detergent or dispersal additive is used to keep the carbon particles in suspension in the oil so that the filters remove them. Other additives strengthen the oil film under boundary friction conditions, and reduce the effect of temperature on the viscosity of the oil. Yet another additive reduces the corrosive effect of exhaust gases which dissolve in the oil to form acids, this action being assisted by a good system of crankcase ventilation which ensures a stream of clean air through the engine to sweep out the 'by-blow' gases. Upper-cylinder lubricants may be added to the petrol to ensure adequate lubrication when the engine is new.

Two-stroke oil
This oil is mixed with the petrol and has wear and corrosion additives or inhibitors. It is also designed to reduce the common two-stroke fault of plug whiskering, in which a thread is built up between the electrodes, eventually putting the plug out of action.

Diesel oils
These are generally similar to those for petrol engines, but the higher bearing pressures in diesel engines necessitate the use of additives which further strengthen the oil film. Many of these oils are detergent oils which reduce the tendency of the piston rings to stick in their grooves. These contain metallic soaps which enclose carbon and dirt particles and so keep them moving with the oil until picked up by the filters.

Oil deterioration

The high temperatures and pressures to which engine oil is subjected cause it to break down and become less efficient. The main causes and their effects are:

1. High temperature. This results in the oxidation of the oil and the formation of acids, and of lacquers which coat all parts of the engine. Friction, heat and wear are all increased.

2. Carbon deposits. These form in the combustion chambers and in the ring grooves. They result in overheating and detonation, and in poor piston sealing. Power output is reduced and fuel is wasted. Excessive carbon is also passed into the oil.

3. Sludge. This is a greasy black substance consisting of carbon particles scraped from the cylinder walls by the rings, water from inside the crankcase, unburnt fuel, dissolved exhaust gases, and grit drawn in through the carburettor and crankcase breather. Minute metal particles may also be present.

4. *Exhaust gases.* Some exhaust gas always escapes past the rings and dissolves in the hot oil to form acids which attack the bearings and other parts of the engine.

5. *Oil dilution.* This results from excessive use of very rich starting mixtures. Liquid petrol passes down the bores into the oil, wasting fuel, washing the oil from the pistons and bores, and causing more wear. It also thins the oil and destroys its cushioning properties in the bearings. Normally this petrol is dispersed as the engine warms up.

6. *Oil contamination.* This is similar to dilution but in this case diesel fuel is the contaminant, and the oil has to be changed. Usually some fault in the pump or governor gives an excess of fuel which is not burnt in the usual way.

ENGINE LUBRICATION SYSTEM

Components

Modern lubrication systems are all of the forced-feed type in which the oil is fed into the crankshaft main and big-end bearings under a pressure of between 200 kN/m^2 and 600 kN/m^2. A well-designed system will have the following components:

(1) A sump or tank.
(2) A pump or pumps.
(3) A pressure relief valve or bleed.
(4) A pressure gauge or warning lamp and switch.
(5) A system of pipes or ducts to direct oil to the bearings.
(6) Wire-gauze filters to protect the pumps, and filters with fine fabric or paper elements to protect the bearings from dirt.
(7) A system of crankcase venting to reduce formation of acids in the oil.

Types of system
Wet sump

In this, the type most often used in vehicle engines, all the oil required is carried in the sump bolted to the underside of the crankcase.

Dry sump

In this type most of the oil required is carried in a separate tank. The sump is small and acts only as a collecting tray for the oil which has passed through the bearings. Two pumps are used, the smaller drawing oil from the tank and forcing it through the bearings and the larger returning the oil to the tank. The larger pump is known as the scavenge pump.

Dry-sump types are used where the space under the engine is limited, e.g. in motor cycles, but some racing cars and very heavy commercial vehicles use this system because it permits the use of larger quantities of oil. This oil is passed through coolers before returning to the tank and so acts as a much more efficient coolant.

The wet sump system

Oil distribution

The oil is distributed to the various engine components by either forced feed, splash, or oil mist. The parts running at the highest speeds and under the highest loads are lubricated by oil under pressure, and fluid friction occurs in their bearings, e.g. crankshaft main and big-ends. The remaining parts are fed by oil which is splashed out from these bearings, and boundary friction occurs between their bearing surfaces. The pistons and rings operate under conditions of both fluid and boundary friction.

Pressure feeds. The oil pump delivers oil under pressure into the gallery pipe which extends for the full length of the crankcase. Each main bearing is connected to this gallery by holes drilled through the crankcase webs, and similar drilled holes are used to connect the camshaft bearings to the gallery. The crankshaft webs are drilled to permit the oil to pass through into the big-end bearings. These drilled holes enable the oil under pressure to lubricate all these bearings *at the same time*. If hydraulic tappets are used, these may use the same oil supply after extra filtering. Connections are also made from the gallery to the oil-pressure gauge or warning-lamp switch, and to the rocker shaft of the overhead valve gear. In many engines the timing gears or chains are lubricated by a spray of pressure oil. In all these secondary feeds the *quantity* is restricted by the use of small bore pipes or some other form of restrictor.

Splash feeds. The oil which escapes from the big-end bearings is

splashed all around the inside of the crankcase and so supplies
generous quantities of oil to the cams and tappets, and to the oil
pump and distributor driving gears. In many engines this oil is
sufficient to provide lubrication for the cylinder bores and pistons,
and gudgeon pins. It also helps to cool the piston crowns. The
excess oil is scraped from the bores by the scraper rings and is returned to the sump via small holes drilled through the piston. In

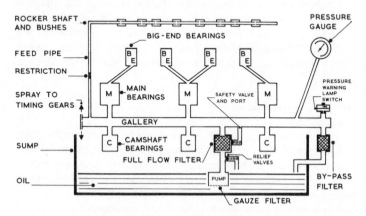

Fig. 4.1 Lubrication system

some engines a more positive supply of oil may be needed for the
cylinder bores. This is arranged for by means of a jet of oil sprayed
through a small hole drilled in the shell and body of the big-end,
the spray occurring each time the drilled hole in the upper half of
the big end of the connecting rod coincides with the main feed hole
drilled in the crankpin (see Fig. 3.1). In some engines the connecting
rod is drilled up its length, so that pressure oil is also fed to the small-
end bushes. A small side drilling from the main drilling may be used
to lubricate the thrust side of the cylinder bore.

Mist feeds. The inside of the crankcase and valve chamber are filled
by an oil mist as the various parts move at high speeds. This mist
provides adequate lubrication for all those parts not lubricated by
pressure or splash. Valve stems and springs are often lubricated by
mist, although the modern tendency is to provide for their lubrication by oil jets or feeds through holes drilled in the rocker arms.

Sumps

The sump of the wet-sump system acts both as an oil tank and as an oil cooler. The sump is made of pressed steel or cast aluminium alloy and is placed in the air stream which passes under the vehicle. In this way the air can carry away sufficient heat to maintain the oil temperature within the limits of 50 °C to 110 °C. Aluminium-alloy sumps may be finned to increase their heat-dissipating area.

The sumps of car engines vary in capacity from about 2 litres to about 9 litres; those of commercial vehicles may hold about 14 litres.

A sump must have an indicator to show the quantity of oil in the sump at any time. This may be a dip stick, or an electrical device consisting of a resistance which is varied by the movements of a float on the surface of the oil, a gauge on the instrument panel responding to the resistance changes and indicating the quantity of oil in the sump.

A drain plug is fitted to the sump to enable the oil to be changed. This plug is sometimes magnetized and so attracts any minute particles of iron and steel from the oil.

Pumps

The oil pumps are usually mounted on the underside of the crank-case and are driven from the camshaft by skew gears. The body of the pump is immersed in the oil and a drilled hole connects the pumping chamber with the main oil gallery. The relief valve may be arranged from this drilling or from the gallery itself. A number of different pumps are available but they all operate on the same principle – enclosing a small volume of oil and forcing it into a system already full of oil. Each separate volume of oil is forced into the system at a faster rate than oil can escape from the system, and so the pressure built up is really a back pressure. The efficiency of these pumps therefore depends upon how completely they seal off the volume of oil from the sump. Submerging the pump chamber in the oil makes this sealing more effective by reducing the chance of air leaking into the pump. It also makes the pump self priming.

Pump filters. The pressure differences which cause the oil to enter the pump chamber are quite small, so the filter, which protects the pump from the larger particles of dirt and metal, must offer only a very slight resistance to the flow of oil. Such filters are made from a fairly coarse wire gauze and are arranged across the intake of the pump chamber.

Constant level intake. The arrangement of the intake close to the bottom of the sump has two disadvantages. The first is that any accumulated dirt and sludge will be drawn into the pump and may ultimately damage the bearings. The second is that the level of the oil varies during acceleration and cornering of the vehicle, so affecting the rate at which oil flows into the pump. This may result in fluctuation of the oil pressure and possible bearing failure due to oil starvation. These disadvantages may be overcome by the use of a floating pick-up. One end of the pick-up pipe is fitted into the intake of the pump chamber and is free to pivot. The other end is attached to the underside of a metal float and surrounded by a wire gauze filter. The float follows the movement of the oil surface and the flow of oil into the pump does not vary. Dirt cannot be drawn into the pump because the entry never reaches the bottom of the sump.

Gallery pipe

This is a hole running the full length of the crankcase and it may be cast or drilled. In large engines a separate pipe may be used. Both ends are sealed, and detachable plugs may be used to facilitate cleaning. Oil is delivered from the drilling in the pump body into the gallery and is then distributed to the various pressure-fed bearings.

Eccentric vane pump

This is an older type used for pressures of between 200 kN/m^2 and 350 kN/m^2. It consists of a spindle which carries two or four vanes and which is arranged off-centre, or eccentrically, in relation to the surrounding case. The vanes may be spring-loaded to maintain contact with the case, or rely upon centrifugal force. Oil enters at the point where the volume in the chamber is largest and is swept around the case. As it is swept around, the volume is reduced slightly and oil is discharged into the gallery. This type is more positive in its sealing than the gear type, but the rate of vane-edge wear results in a relatively short service life.

Gear pump

This type is very commonly used; it has a long life and requires very little attention. It consists of two spur gears, only one of which is driven by the camshaft, which rotate inside a close-fitting case. It is *not* a centrifugal pump, and oil passes around the casing and not through the centre. Each tooth traps a small quantity of oil and carries it around the case before discharging it into the gallery. The

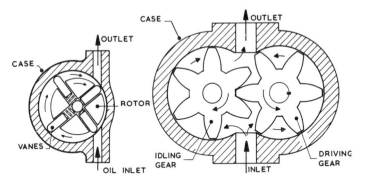

Fig. 4.2 Eccentric vane pump   Fig. 4.3 Gear pump

sealing is not positive and these pumps are not self-priming. They are therefore usually submerged in the oil. In some engines two of these pumps are built into one casing, one being a feed pump and one a scavenge pump. Types that are mounted outside the oil must be hand primed if the system has been disturbed or not operated for some time.

Plunger pump

This type is positive in its sealing and, because it has a much greater lift, can be mounted outside the sump if so required. It may be used for medium and high-pressure systems and two such pumps may be used together to reduce oil pulsation. Plunger pumps are not often now used in engines, but are used in overdrive units, usually in conjunction with a pressure reservoir or accumulator.

The upward movement of the plunger, due to its spring, draws oil from the sump through the large, inlet, ball valve into the pump chamber. When the eccentric forces the plunger down, the inlet ball is forced shut and the smaller, outlet ball forced from its seating. Oil passes through this valve and through the holes drilled in the plunger, to be discharged into the gallery.

Failure is usually due to dirt on the valve seats, or to excessive travel of the ball valves because of wear and distortion of the stop pins.

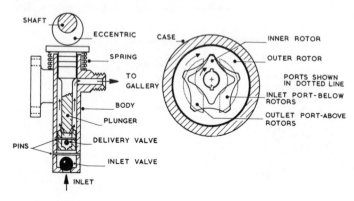

Fig. 4.4 Plunger pump   Fig. 4.5 Rotor pump

Rotor pump
Because of its much better sealing, this type is about 25 % more efficient than the gear pump and has a longer life in service. It is often used in engine systems, but is also very suitable for use in hydraulic, transmission, and vacuum systems.

The pump consists of inner and outer rotors which revolve against each other inside a cylindrical casing. The inner rotor is carried on a shaft eccentric to the drive shaft. The outer rotor has a set of internal lobes of the same shape as the inner but one more in number, and rotates about the same axis as the drive shaft. The lobe shapes are designed to ensure very good sealing contact. Delivery and inlet ports are arranged in the top and bottom of the casing.

The method of operation is the same as that of the eccentric-vane type but it is free of that pump's disadvantages. A spring-loaded ball or plunger type of relief valve may be fitted.

Relief valve
As the pump must be designed to provide adequate oil pressure at very low engine speeds, it follows that at higher engine speeds the

pressures may well become excessively high, resulting in a higher oil consumption as more oil is thrown up the cylinder bores, and in the possibility of damage to the weaker parts of the system, i.e. oil seals and small pipes and connections. Excessively high pressures may also be produced when the oil is cold and thicker (more viscous). These excessively high pressures are reduced or avoided by the use of the relief valve.

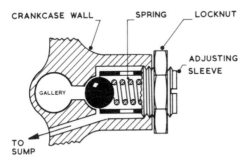

Fig. 4.6 External relief valve

The relief valve consists of a spring-loaded ball or plunger, the position of which controls the leakage, or escape, of oil through a port leading from the enclosed system back into the sump. The valve may be arranged between the pump chamber and the gallery; in the gallery; or in the head casting of a full-flow type of filter. The normal operating pressure of the oil is determined by the force exerted on ball or plunger by the spring. When this pressure is exceeded, the ball is forced from its seat by the excessive pressure and oil escapes back into the sump – so reducing the pressure to that determined by the combination of (a) the rate of escape of oil from the bearings, and (b) the rate of escape through the relief valve. The spring-loading of the valve may be adjustable. In practice, the relief valve is usually open slightly at idling speeds and opens more and more as the engine speed is increased.

Oil filters

Two main types of filters are used and both are fitted into the delivery or pressure side of the system. Usually only one type is fitted in an engine but some engines have both.

By-pass filter

This type is fitted between the main oil gallery and the sump, so that part of the oil delivered by the pump flows straight through this filter and returns to the sump. The filter consists of a head casting, which is bolted to the crankcase and has internal connections to the gallery and the sump, and a pressed-steel case which encloses a paper or fabric filtering element. The element is sealed inside the case in such a way that the high-pressure oil cannot leave the case except by passing through the element and leaving all the dirt and carbon particles trapped in it. According to type, the element may be either washed in petrol or replaced at mileages specified by the engine manufacturer. Most modern filters use replaceable elements.

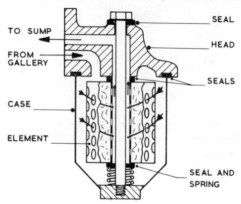

Fig. 4.7 By-pass filter

About one-tenth of the pump delivery is passed through this filter, and the complete contents of the sump are filtered about twelve times an hour at normal road speeds.

The element of this type of filter can be designed to remove very small particles of dirt because the rate of filtration is slow and the supply of pressure oil to the bearings is not restricted by it.

Some designs of by-pass filter have the element sealed into the case. When these elements become choked by dirt the whole unit is replaced. If the elements of by-pass filters do become choked by dirt no more filtering is done and the bearings are supplied by oil which grows steadily more and more fouled and dirty.

Full flow filter

This type is fitted between the pump and the gallery, and consists of a filtering element enclosed by a detachable case. The filter head is bolted to the crankcase and in many such filters the oil-pressure relief valve is built into this head. The head also incorporates a safety device which allows unfiltered oil to pass to the bearings

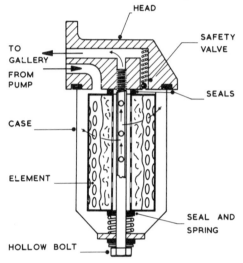

Fig. 4.8 Full flow filter

if the element should become choked. This device is a spring-loaded ball valve which controls an alternative path for the oil between the pump and the gallery, the ball being forced from its seat by the pressure build-up when the oil cannot pass through the element.

The element is sealed in such a way that the oil from the pump cannot leave the case to pass to the bearings without passing through the element, or through the safety valve. Because this element is between the pump and the bearings, it must be designed to restrict the flow of oil as little as possible. Full-flow elements cannot therefore filter out such fine particles as by-pass elements, and their volume must be larger.

OIL SEALING

The various joint faces of the engine must be made oil-tight, and kept oil-tight, to reduce oil consumption. This oil sealing is usually accomplished by the use of gaskets of thin waxed paper, of cork, or of a special material which is resistant to heat, water, and oil. The thicker the gasket the more important it is to tighten the joint evenly.

The sealing of the crankcase at each end of the crankshaft has been described in the section on the crankshaft.

CRANKCASE VENTILATION

It is necessary to arrange for a constant stream of fresh air to pass through the crankcase while the engine is running, to reduce the contamination of the oil by petrol vapour or exhaust gases. Such contamination forms acids in the oil which corrode the bearing surfaces and may cause bearing failure. Water vapour is also removed and this reduces the formation of sludge.

Some engines were fitted with an extractor pipe which was brought down into the airstream under the vehicle, the motion of the vehicle causing the foul air to be drawn out while fresh air was drawn in at the top of the crankcase.

Many modern engines have a positive system of ventilation in which foul air is drawn out of the crankcase into the inlet manifold. The foul air is replaced by fresh air which is passed through a wire-gauze air cleaner before it enters the crankcase, the air cleaner being in the carburettor cleaner or in the oil filler cap.

OIL-PRESSURE GAUGE

The gauge is mounted on the instrument panel and consists of a flattened, thin-walled, tube which is curved and sealed at one end. This is known as a Bourdon tube. The open end of the tube is clamped to the base of the instrument and is connected to the main oil gallery by a small-diameter copper pipe. Any oil pressure in the gallery also acts in the tube and tries to make it straighten out. The slight movement of the sealed end is magnified by a lever and quadrant, and causes a needle to move over a scale to indicate the pressure in kilonewtons per square metre.

Note that these gauges only indicate pressure of oil entering the bearings and NOT the quantity of oil in the sump.

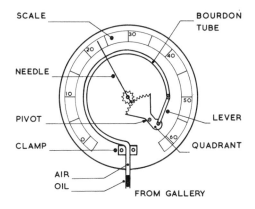

Fig. 4.9 Oil pressure gauge

OIL WARNING LAMP

The lamp usually shows a coloured light and is mounted on the instrument panel. The passage of electric current through the lamp is controlled by an oil-pressure switch, the ignition switch acting as a master switch.

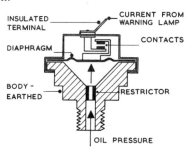

Fig. 4.10 Pressure switch

The pressure switch consists of a fixed insulated contact and an earthed contact which is mounted on a flexible steel diaphragm subject to the oil pressure in the gallery. The contacts are normally closed, but when the oil pressure reaches or exceeds about 50 kN/m^2 the diaphragm is flexed and the contacts are separated, so causing the lamp to go out and to indicate that pressure high enough to be safe is being produced. Note that this arrangement only shows adequate pressure and not the actual pressure.

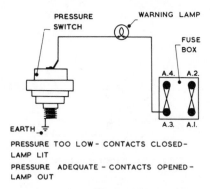

PRESSURE TOO LOW - CONTACTS CLOSED-
LAMP LIT
PRESSURE ADEQUATE - CONTACTS OPENED -
LAMP OUT

Fig. 4.11 Circuit for oil-pressure warning lamp

OIL PRESSURES AND FAULTS

The oil pressure shown on the gauge is really the measure of the back pressure produced by the pump delivering oil into the system at a much faster rate than that at which it can escape from the bearings. Normally the relief valve is open all the time after tick-over to protect the system from excessively high pressures. If the bearings are excessively worn no amount of adjusting at the relief valve will increase the pressure – once the normal operating temperatures are reached.

The oil pressure is so important to the life of the engine, that abnormal gauge readings call for an immediate check to ascertain the cause. The common faults and their probable causes are:

No pressure shown
(1) No oil in sump.
(2) Pipe from gallery to gauge choked by dirt, or broken.

(3) If warning lamp fitted – bulb burned out, or wire broken, or pressure switch damaged, i.e. no light when ignition switched on.
(4) Gauge broken.
(5) Relief valve stuck in the open position.
(6) Spring of relief valve broken, or valve stuck in open position.
(7) Pump filter completely choked by dirt.
(8) Oil pump not working due to sheared drive shaft, excessive wear, or large internal air leak.

Low gauge pressure
(1) Gauge giving a reading less than actual pressure.
(2) Oil too thin, or engine too hot.
(3) Relief valve stuck part open – damaged or dirty seat, valve or spring.
(4) Spring of relief valve weak or adjusted too lightly.
(5) Pump filter partly choked.
(6) Internal oil leak on pressure side of system – cracked gallery pipe or web ducts. Loose unions if separate gallery pipe.
(7) Slack or excessively worn main and/or big-end bearings.

High gauge pressure
(1) Gauge reading above actual pressure.
(2) Oil too thick, or engine cold.
(3) Relief valve stuck closed.
(4) Tension of spring on relief valve too high.
(5) Oil ducts in pressure side of system partly choked.

Occasionally the oil supply to the operating gear of the overhead valve is interrupted; this is caused by the obstruction of the feed duct or pipe, usually at the restrictor, or by the pipe being broken. Sometimes one rocker arm may be starved of oil; this is usually caused by the oil feed holes being choked up.

If blue exhaust smoke is produced when the engine is accelerated after ticking over or coasting, it is a good indication that the pistons and cylinders are nearing the end of their useful life.

5

Fuel Supply

Function

This is to transfer fuel from a low-level tank to a carburettor float chamber at higher level, at a rate greater than the maximum rate of engine fuel consumption. Most pumps are capable of delivering up to a height of 2 m but about 0·45 m is the usual requirement.

Construction

The pump is bolted to the side of the engine and is operated by an eccentric on the engine camshaft. Metal pipes are used to connect

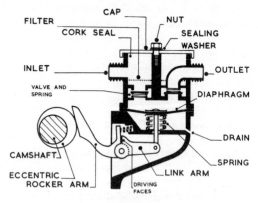

Fig. 5.1 Mechanical fuel pump

the pump to the tank and to the float chamber. The pump is an assembly of die-castings which form a sediment chamber and a pumping chamber, the incoming petrol first passing through a fine wire-gauze filter. The pumping chamber has a flexible wall in the form of a rubberized fabric diaphragm which is moved inward by the action of a spring, and outward by the action of a link arm. This link arm is mounted upon the same pivot as the rocker arm and the two normally act as a solid lever, a contact face being formed on each. The rocker arm is spring-loaded in such a way that it always maintains contact with the camshaft eccentric. Opposed disc-type, spring-loaded valves are fitted to control the flow of petrol into and out of the pumping chamber, the movement of the fuel being caused by the pressure changes resulting from the movement of the diaphragm. It is important to note that, although the rocker arm always maintains contact with the eccentric, it may not always be able to move the link arm.

Operation

(*a*) *Intake stroke.* As the engine camshaft rotates, the eccentric lifts the rocker arm which forces the link arm and the diaphragm down, and compresses the diaphragm spring. This outward movement of the diaphragm increases the volume of the chamber and so reduces the pressure inside it. The difference between this pressure and the higher atmospheric pressure in the tank forces petrol to flow from the tank, open the inlet valve against its spring, and fill the chamber. The outlet valve is held closed by both its spring and the pressure difference. When the chamber is full the pressures are equalized and the inlet valve is closed by its spring.

(*b*) *Delivery stroke.* Continued camshaft rotation removes the lifting force from the rocker arm but its spring causes it to maintain contact with the eccentric. The link arm and the diaphragm are now forced up by the diaphragm spring. This reduces the volume of the chamber and therefore increases the pressure on the petrol inside it. The inlet valve is closed more firmly to its seat and the difference between the pressure in the chamber and atmospheric pressure in the float chamber opens the outlet valve and forces petrol to flow into the float chamber. The delivery pressure is derived from the diaphragm spring and is normally between 14 kN/m^2 and 28 kN/m^2.

(*c*) *Idling stroke.* When the float chamber is filled to its correct level, delivery is stopped by the action of the float-operated needle valve. This prevents the pump diaphragm spring extending and the diaphragm and link arm are held in their down position. Under these conditions the rocker arm follows the eccentric, but its face cannot contact the face of the link arm. The diaphragm cannot therefore be moved, and the pump idles until such time as the float needle valve is opened again. When this occurs the diaphragm is able to move inward to start a new delivery stroke.

Maintenance

Clean filter and sediment trap. Do not use rag. Renew sealing washer and cover gasket.

Table 5.1 Faults and causes

Fault	Causes
No delivery	Tank empty. Choked supply pipe. Choked pump filter. Float needle stuck closed. Air leak at pump set screw or gasket. Slack unions. Tank vent blocked. Pump valves dirty. Hole in diaphragm. Diaphragm screws slack. Spring broken
Leakage at diaphragm	Diaphragm screws slack: slacken off evenly – stretch diaphragm – tighten screws across unit
Flooding at carburettor	Pump mounting gasket too thin. Rocker arm bent outward. Diaphragm spring too strong. Float needle and seat worn or dirty. Pump link arm or pivots damaged. Float punctured
Pump noisy	Always due to a mechanical failure. Worn spindle or levers. Broken springs

System faults

Pumps are often blamed for faults outside the actual unit, e.g. slack unions, damaged pipes, and dirt in the tank. Modern vehicles are sometimes troubled by vapour locks in the pipes which result in either an excessively rich mixture in the manifold or no fuel delivery. This fault may be caused by a choked manifold drain, or by the pump, pipes or float chamber receiving too much of the heat radiated by the exhaust manifold; shielding may be required.

ELECTRICAL PETROL PUMP

Construction

The pump-chamber action is similar to that of the mechanical pump but the valves are not spring-loaded. The diaphragm is moved outward from the chamber by the action of an electromagnet which attracts an iron disc attached to the diaphragm. The operation of

the magnet is controlled by toggle-operated contacts activated by
a link rod also attached to the diaphragm. The link rod is centralized
by a set of non-magnetic rollers, and the diaphragm is moved into
the chamber by a spring. The flow of battery current to the unit is
controlled by the ignition switch.

Operation

(*a*) *Intake stroke.* When the contact points are closed and the ignition
is switched on, battery current is passed through the electromagnet
to earth, so energizing the magnet and attracting to it the iron disc

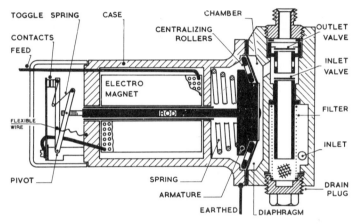

Fig. 5.2 Electrical fuel pump

attached to the diaphragm. The diaphragm is drawn outward from
the chamber, compressing its spring and increasing the volume of
the chamber. A pressure reduction is caused and the difference between this pressure and the higher atmospheric pressure in the tank
forces petrol to flow from the tank, open the inlet valve, and fill the
chamber – passing through a filter before passing through the inlet
valve. As the chamber is filled the pressures equalize and the inlet
valve is closed by gravity. As the diaphragm reaches the full extent
of its outward movement, the attached link rod throws over the
toggle and the contacts are opened in one quick movement.

(*b*) *Delivery stroke.* When the contacts are separated, the current cannot energize the electromagnet and the diaphragm spring therefore forces the diaphragm back into the chamber. The chamber volume is reduced and the pressure on the petrol inside it increased. This closes the inlet valve more firmly to its seat and the pressure difference between the chamber and the float chamber opens the outlet valve and forces petrol into the float chamber. Note that once again it is the diaphragm spring which causes the petrol delivery.

(*c*) *Idling stroke.* When the float chamber is full the float needle valve stops delivery by holding the diaphragm in its outward position. The link rod has thrown over the toggle and therefore the electromagnet cannot be energized. When the petrol level falls and the needle valve opens again the delivery is made, the link arm moves the toggle to close the contacts, and the intake stroke is started again.

Maintenance

Clean filter. Lightly oil toggle pivots. Check delivery pressure – about 14 kN/m^2. Clean and reset contacts to 0·76 mm.

Special high-pressure types are available and these are about 19 mm longer than the standard types. The two types are not interchangeable and fuel starvation will result if a high-pressure type is replaced by a standard type. Insulated-return and dual pumps are also available.

Table 5.2   Faults and causes

Mechanical faults	*Causes*
No delivery	Tank empty. Supply pipe blocked – slacken intake union – pump should tick. Delivery pipe blocked – slacken union – pump should tick. Dirt in filter and valves. Float needle stuck closed
Noisy operation	Air leaks on intake side. Petrol leaks on delivery side
Electrical faults	*Causes*
No operation	No current supply – broken wires. Toggle mechanism seized – rusted. Dirty or burned points. Winding shorted to earth, or broken

THE PRACTICAL CARBURETTOR

Vehicle carburettors must:

(1) Atomize the liquid fuel as finely as possible in order to obtain the most complete mixing of the fuel with the air.

(2) Provide the correct *mass* of mixture to suit each and every condition of engine speed and load.

(3) Provide the correct *strength* of mixture to suit each and every combination of engine speed and load.

(4) Provide easy starting when the engine is cold.

(5) Enable the engine to idle or run steadily at a low speed.

(6) Provide maximum acceleration, without flat spots, when the throttle is opened.

(7) Provide the maximum fuel economy possible under all operating conditions.

(8) Be capable of adjustment to meet different atmospheric temperature and pressure conditions, and to permit the use of different qualities and types of fuel.

(9) Have the least possible number of wearing parts, be compact, and be easy to service.

Atomization

The breaking up of the liquid fuel into very minute liquid drops is called atomization. This occurs naturally when the liquid is delivered into a fast-moving stream of air. Adequate atomization is obtained by the careful selection of the diameter of the venturi, and this is based upon the speed of the air flow through the main air tube at the lowest engine operating speed. If the venturi diameter is correct, the degree of atomization at the lowest air speed will be adequate; much better atomization will be produced at all higher speeds.

The axis of the venturi may be horizontal, vertical, or inclined. The vertical and the inclined types are the most common today and result in the carburettor being classed as a down-draught or semi-down-draught type. These have the advantage that the air flow is assisted by gravity. They are also more accessible because they are mounted near the top of the engine.

Jets

These are screwed brass plugs pierced by accurately sized holes. They are used to limit the maximum rate of flow of air or liquid under specified conditions, i.e. the head of fuel behind the jet and the pressure difference between the two sides of the jet.

Mixture mass or quantity

When the pistons are moved down their cylinders on their induction strokes, they create a depression inside their cylinders. The *difference* between the pressure in the cylinders and the atmospheric pressure outside forces air to pass through the carburettor main air tube and the manifold, and to charge the cylinders. The quantity of mixture passing to the cylinders is controlled by the use of a disc-type throttle valve. This has the effect of varying the volumetric efficiency and so controls the speed and power output of the engine.

If the engine is over-loaded the piston speed is reduced, and so therefore is the air speed. This reduces the quantity of mixture flowing into the cylinders and also reduces the power output of the engine – although the throttle may be fully open.

The throttle spindle must be so arranged in the main air tube that the mixture will be distributed equally between the two ends of the intake manifold. In most engines this is obtained by arranging the spindle axis parallel with that of the manifold. The throttle is always at the manifold end of the main air tube.

Mixture strength or quality

The strength of the mixture required for a particular operating condition may be obtained by selecting the size of jet which will permit the correct mass of fuel to pass into the air stream, i.e. the correct mass of fuel is matched up to the mass of air entering the engine.

Correction or compensation

The simple carburettor can only supply the correct strength of mixture for one very limited range of air speeds. At air speeds below this range the mixture is too weak, and at air speeds above this range it is too rich. This fault in the strength of the mixture delivered may be corrected, or compensated for, by one of three methods:

(a) By using a fixed size of venturi and (1) reducing the fuel supply at high speeds by air bleeds and (2) increasing the fuel supply at low speeds by drawing upon a reserve well of fuel (Zenith).

(b) By using a fixed size of venturi and controlling both the fuel and the air supply by immersed air bleeds (Solex).

(c) By altering the venturi and the jet sizes at the same time (SU).

Carburettors based upon principles (a) and (b) are known as fixed-venturi variable-depression types and those based upon principle (c) are known as constant-vacuum (depression) variable-choke (venturi) types. The latter may also be known as mechanical types because their main components move in operation.

When the word 'correction' is used in relation to carburettors, it refers to the method by which the variations of the air speed through the venturi are prevented from altering the mixture strength from that required under particular operating conditions.

A *corrected* carburettor system is one which delivers the *same strength* of mixture at all air speeds after idling. An uncompensated or *under-compensated* system is one which delivers a progressively *richer* mixture as the air speed increases, i.e. the simple carburettor. An *over-compensated* system is one which delivers a progressively *weaker* mixture as the air speed is increased.

In the Zenith and some other carburettors, a compound system is used in which an under-compensated system is used in conjunction with an over-compensated system. The faults of the first are compensated by the second, and by the careful matching up of the sizes of the two fuel jets the correct mixture strengths for all conditions after idling may be obtained. The operation of this method is described in the section dealing with the Zenith carburettor.

In the Solex and some other carburettors the air-bleed system is used. This is similar in arrangement to the over-compensated system of the Zenith carburettor but the air supply or bleed into the system is controlled by an air-correction jet and a diffuser tube. These are in addition to the fuel jet, and the degree of correction and the mixture strength at any speed after idling can be obtained by the careful selection of the sizes of the air-correction and fuel jets. The operation of this method is described in the section dealing with the Solex carburettor.

In the constant-vacuum carburettors, the increase in the air flow automatically increases the sizes of both the venturi and the fuel jet. The variation in jet size is produced by the use of a tapered needle which is attached to the moving side of the venturi and which dips into the fuel jet. The taper of the needle determines the fuel supply at any venturi position and so controls the strength of the mixture supplied. This action is described in the section on the SU carburettor.

PRACTICAL MIXTURE STRENGTHS

The air : fuel ratios given in this section are only approximate. Slight variations will occur between different types of carburettor and engine.

Cold starting (full choke)

In the early days of the motor vehicle, the rich mixtures needed for starting were obtained by the use of an air-limiting valve, or a strangler. This became known as the choke and this term is still applied to the starting device – although it may be quite different in construction and operation from the early strangler. In this sense the difference is not very important, but the word choke is also used to describe the venturi. Students must take care to use the correct word or confusion will result.

A vehicle engine must start readily from cold and, to make this possible, three main difficulties must be overcome.

The first is that when the crankshaft is rotated by hand, or by the starter motor, the resulting speed of the air through the venturi is low. The depression created is therefore not large enough to produce a delivery of fuel from the main and compensating systems or their equivalent. This difficulty is overcome by the use of a strangler valve, a separate starting carburettor, or a device which increases the size of the fuel jet for starting.

The second difficulty is that under cold conditions only a part of the liquid fuel will vaporize. This part consists of the lighter fractions of the petrol and the mixture entering the *manifold* will be weak. It is then weakened further because some of the fuel which has vaporized and atomized is condensed into larger liquid drops by the cold walls of the manifold. The mixture which finally passes into the *cylinders* will be so weak that it will either fail to ignite or will produce insufficient power to keep the engine running. This difficulty is overcome by supplying an excessive quantity of fuel to compensate for the losses. The usual mixture strength for these conditions is about four parts of air to one of fuel by weight, i.e. 4:1.

Cold running (half choke)
The third difficulty arises when the engine fires and runs under its own power. At this point the air supply is being limited but the venturi depression is being greatly increased by the increased speed of the pistons. The consequence is that even more fuel is delivered by the main and compensating systems or their equivalent, or by the starter carburettor. This excessively rich mixture must only be used for a very short time, and all modern carburettors have some device which enables this strength of mixture to be reduced to between six and eight to one, i.e. 6–8:1.

This reduction may be made by manual or automatic control. At the same time the throttle linkage is operated to provide a fast idling speed.

The use of the 4:1 mixture must not be prolonged. If it is used for too long, and if the weakening device fails to operate, the following will result:

(a) The lubricating oil will be washed off the cylinder walls, pistons and rings by the liquid petrol. This will result in extra wear as the friction is increased.

(b) The lubricating oil will be diluted as the liquid petrol passes down the cylinder bores. While this may at first help to reduce the load on the starter motor it will then result in extra bearing wear and possible bearing hammering as the oil cushion is destroyed.

(c) Carbon deposits will build up rapidly in the combustion chamber and in the exhaust ports – leading to overheating and pre-ignition, carbon being a heat insulator.

(d) The combustion chamber and spark plugs will be flooded by liquid petrol, and the engine will cease to operate.

Usually the power loss which occurs under these conditions is so great that the driver is warned, and either puts the choke control to the shut-off position or investigates the cause of the failure of the automatic weakening device.

Warm idling (choke fully off)
Once normal engine operating temperatures are reached, the choke control must be in the fully off position. Under warm idling

conditions, the throttle valve is almost closed and consequently a large depression exists in the inlet manifold. At the same time the low speed of the engine results in only a small quantity of exhaust gas moving relatively slowly through the exhaust manifold. When the inlet valves are open, on valve overlap, the pressure difference causes some exhaust gas to be induced with the fresh charges of mixture. This reduces the mass of mixture induced into the cylinders and the resulting power loss is avoided by supplying a slightly richer mixture. The strength of this warm idling mixture is about 10:1; this is sufficient to enable the engine to idle slowly and steadily.

When the engine is idling the throttle valve is almost closed and it therefore becomes the most restrictive part of the main air tube. The depression is formed at its edges and not in the centre of the venturi and a separate U-tube system must be provided to supply fuel. This system delivers fuel to the edge of the throttle through a system of ducts and its mixture strength is adjustable by means of a taper needle controlling an air bleed. In the constant vacuum types the venturi and fuel jet sizes are reduced together so the venturi remains as the greater restriction to the air flow at idling. The single jet can therefore also deliver fuel under idling conditions.

Economical cruising (part throttle openings)
Under conditions of light engine loadings and part throttle openings the petrol engine can use weak mixtures with no danger of over-heating and burning of the valves. Under these conditions the slight loss of power that results is not noticeable, and the fuel saving is a distinct advantage. The mixture strength for economical cruising is between 15:1 and 17:1.

Acceleration
A slightly enriched mixture is required for steady acceleration, and in many carburettors this is obtained automatically by limiting the degree of correction or compensation exerted by the compensating system. The mixture strength is about 12:1.

In some designs the sudden opening of the throttle results in a sudden weakening of the mixture, the consequent sudden power loss being called a 'flat spot'. Flat spots may be overcome by the use of some form of accelerator pump which supplies extra fuel at that point to overcome the temporary weak mixture.

Full power (full throttle)

A rich mixture is needed for full-throttle operation in order to obtain the maximum possible heating of the air in the mixture. The strength is about 12:1 and may be progressively reduced as the momentum of the vehicle is increased.

6

Carburettors

This is a fixed-venturi variable-depression type. The main air tube houses the venturi and the throttle valve, and supports the float chamber.

Float chamber
This forms one side of all the U-tube systems and acts as a reservoir to meet the maximum demand for fuel. The chamber is attached to

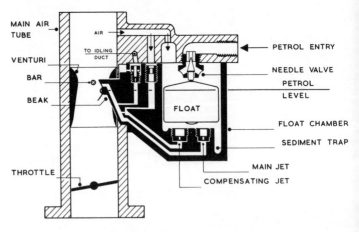

Fig. 6.1 Float chamber and spray system

the main air tube by set bolts or screws and must be vented to atmospheric pressure. In later designs this vent is under the air cleaner, so only filtered air may enter. The jets are submerged in the fuel and so are not affected by the delivery pulsations of the fuel pump. They are arranged slightly above the floor of the chamber to avoid their becoming choked by any fine dirt which may have escaped the various filters in the fuel system. In some arrangements the jets may be removed from the underside of the chamber. This has a series of ducts which connect the jets to the spray beak secured to the side of the chamber.

The level of the fuel in the chamber must be correct. If it is too high, the result will be flooding of the chamber and the manifold, and excessive fuel consumption. If it is too low, delivery delay or 'gulping' will occur. The level is determined by the action of a sealed and hollow float upon a tapered needle valve which controls the entry of fuel from the lift pump. The level may be adjusted by means of washers or shims under the valve assembly.

Spraying system

This is known as the beak and bar assembly. It consists of a small bar, set at right angles to the throttle spindle across the narrowest part of the venturi, and a spray beak which is mounted on the side of the detachable float chamber and which protrudes into the centre of the venturi. The sloping side of the beak is arranged towards the engine side of the air tube, and creates a small depression which helps to reduce the size of the small drops of liquid fuel. The emerging fuel is caught by the bar and is spread evenly over the whole bore of the air tube – so providing both a very fine atomization of the liquid fuel and its more even distribution across the area of the bore.

In operation, the compensator and idling systems both bleed a small amount of air into the fuel in the spray-beak system. This provides a degree of pre-mixing or emulsifying which gives more complete atomization of the liquid fuel.

Starting device

When the engine speed is very low, i.e. at hand or starter-motor cranking speeds, the speed of the air through the main air tube is so low that the resulting pressure difference between the float chamber and the spray beak is not large enough to force fuel to flow from the spray beak. In the Zenith carburettor this difficulty is overcome by the use of a strangler valve.

This valve consists of a circular disc mounted on a spindle arranged in the upper end of the main air tube. The spindle is arranged to one side of the disc centre, and the movement of the spindle and disc cannot be influenced by the control lever, except through the action of a coil spring.

When the lever is pulled over, the valve almost closes the air tube. The piston movements, produced by the starter motor, together with the closing of the air tube, result in the formation of a large

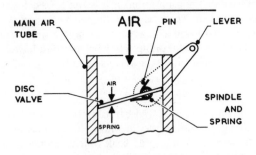

Fig. 6.2 Strangler valve

depression in the air tube. The pressure difference forces a large quantity of fuel to flow from the spray beak to provide a mixture of about 4:1, and the engine fires and runs.

When the engine runs under its own power the increased speeds of the pistons increases the depression and this would increase the strength of the mixture. At this point the increased flow of air results in the disc valve being progressively opened against the action of its spring. This is possible because one side of the disc is made larger than the other by the off-centre arrangement of the spindle, and the entry of more air reduces the mixture strength as the depression is reduced. The mixture strength now will be between 6:1 and 8:1 and the engine can operate at a fast, cold idle.

NOTE. The progressive opening of the disc or strangler valve is controlled by the tension of its spring. This must never be altered during normal service work or the device will fail to operate correctly.

Idling speeds

At idling speeds the throttle is almost closed, and so offers a greater restriction to the air flow than the venturi. This results in the depression being formed at the throttle edges instead of at the venturi centre, and a third U-tube system has to be employed to provide the engine with fuel mixture.

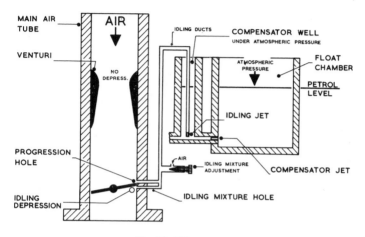

Fig. 6.3. Idling system

One end of this system consists of a jet tube dipping into the compensator well. This is under atmospheric pressure, while the other end of the system of ducts or drillings finishes as a small hole in the wall of the main air tube, close to the throttle edge, which is under the throttle-edge depression. The pressure difference forces fuel to flow from the compensating well through the ducts to the throttle edge. The strength of this mixture is controlled by a taper-ended screw which controls the size of an air bleed into the system; the position of the throttle valve is adjusted by a stop screw. These two screws are adjusted together to obtain a steady idling speed.

Progression hole. When the throttle is opened, its edge moves away from the wall of the air tube. The depression follows this movement and is reduced as the restriction to the air flow is reduced, re-forming in the venturi and increasing as the air speed is increased. It is most important that the change-over from the idling system to the main and compensating system be made as smoothly as possible, i.e. that fuel delivery continues as the position of the depression changes. Failure to maintain delivery under these conditions will result in the sudden production of a weak mixture and the engine will hesitate or 'gulp'. Gulping is overcome by using a second hole in the idling system. The second hole is called the 'progression hole'. This is nearer to the venturi than the first hole. Its use prolongs the final stages of the delivery made by the idling system to allow it to overlap the earlier stages of the delivery made by the main and compensating systems, i.e. it supplies fuel between high idling speeds and low medium speeds.

NOTE. Gulping may be caused in service by:

(a) Dirt obstructing the progression hole.

(b) Dirt obstructing the spray beak.

(c) The fuel level in the float chamber being too low.

Main and compensating systems

The main jet system is the simple carburettor, consisting of a U-tube, a fuel jet, and the venturi. It is an under-compensated system and its faults (the mixture is too weak at low speeds and too rich at high speeds) are corrected by the compensating system which always operates in conjunction with the main jet system. Both

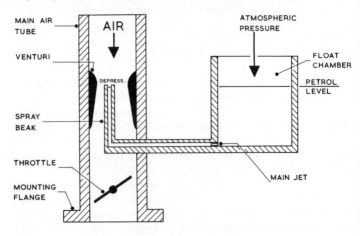

Fig. 6.4 Main jet system

deliver into the spray beak at the same time, this arrangement being known as a compound system.

The compensating system is an over-compensated system which delivers rich mixtures at low air speeds and weaker mixtures as the

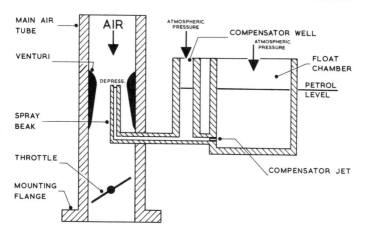

Fig. 6.5 Compensating system

air speed is increased. It is similar in arrangement to the main jet system except that a capacity well, open to atmospheric pressure, is fitted between the jet and the spray beak.

Operation
Lower medium speeds. At engine speeds above that of idling, the depression in the main air tube is formed at the centre of the venturi, around the spray beak. The difference between the pressure in the depression and the atmospheric pressure in the float chamber forces the fuel to flow from both systems, passing into the air stream via the spray beak. The main jet system (simple carburettor) delivers a mixture which is weaker than is required at this speed. The compensating system must therefore supply a richer mixture so that the resulting mixture provided by the two deliveries is of the correct strength. This is possible because the pressure difference acts upon the fuel in the compensator well in addition to that in the float chamber and, in effect, the compensator system makes a double

delivery – one from the well and one through the jet. By selecting the correct relationship of jet sizes for each system the correct mixture strengths can be obtained for the whole speed range after idling.

Medium speed range. As the throttle is opened, the fuel in the compensator is quickly used up and the well cannot be refilled because the jet is limiting the flow from the float chamber. As the main jet is

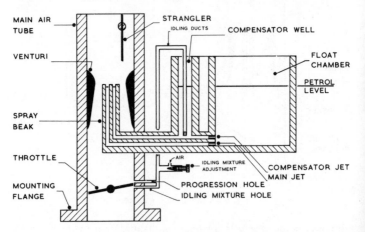

Fig. 6.6 Complete carburettor

also limiting the fuel its system is delivering, the action of the two systems together provides the correct strength of mixture for this speed range.

NOTE. The jet size determines the maximum fuel delivery while the pressure difference determines the size of the delivery up to the maximum.

Medium-to-high speed range. Opening the throttle further cannot result in the main jet system delivering more fuel, but its mixture strength is increased because the increased air flow causes a reduction in the air density. This is corrected by the action of the compensating system. Because the compensating well has been emptied, and its jet is limiting the flow of fuel from the float chamber, this system delivers a progressively weaker mixture as the throttle is opened. This effect is assisted by the fact that air is forced into the system through the well, and so reduces the pressure difference between the spray beak and the float chamber. This air bleed also emulsifies the fuel before it reaches the spray beak and so assists atomization.

The combined operation of these two systems provides the correct mixture strengths for higher running speeds.

Accelerator pump

The particles of fuel in the mixture are heavier than those of air. When the mixture as a whole is suddenly accelerated by the sudden opening of the throttle, the fuel particles take longer than the air to accelerate. They are therefore momentarily left behind and a weak mixture enters the cylinders. This momentarily weak mixture causes the engine to hesitate and probably to spit back through the carburettor – a fault known as an acceleration flat spot.

In some carburettors the compensator system automatically supplies a richer mixture under these conditions and so overcomes the flat spots. In other carburettors an accelerator pump may be fitted.

Function

To automatically increase the mixture strength when the throttle is opened suddenly.

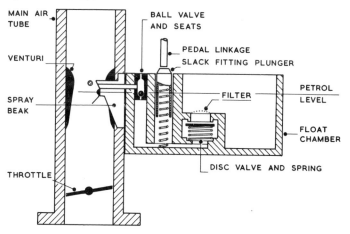

Fig. 6.7 Accelerator pump

Construction

The pump consists of a spring-loaded plunger which is a slack fit in a cylinder formed in the wall of the float chamber. The plunger is forced down by the action of a link rod attached to the throttle linkage and is forced up by the action of its spring. The cylinder is supplied with fuel from the float chamber through a passage, a fine wire-gauze filter and a spring-loaded non-return valve being fitted at the float chamber end. Delivery is made through the spray beak and it is controlled by a small ball valve which has an upper and a lower seat.

Operation

(a) *Sudden throttle opening*. When the throttle is opened suddenly, the plunger is forced down into the cylinder very quickly. The inlet valve is closed by its spring and the delivery ball valve is held closed on its lower seat by its weight, so the plunger movement builds up pressure on the fuel below the plunger. This pressure forces the delivery valve up to its upper seat and allows the fuel to be forced out through the spray beak. This spraying action continues until the pressure falls and allows the delivery ball valve to fall back to its seat, so ending the delivery.

(b) *Recuperation*. When the throttle linkage is released, the plunger is lifted by its spring, and in so doing causes a drop in pressure below the plunger. The difference between this reduced pressure and the higher atmospheric pressure in the float chamber opens the inlet valve and forces fuel to flow through the filter and the valve to refill the pump chamber. As it becomes full and the pressures equalize, the inlet valve is closed by its spring and the pump is ready for its next delivery.

(c) *Slow throttle opening*. When the throttle linkage forces the plunger down slowly no pressure is built up below it because the fuel has time to flow around and over it – due to its very slack fit in the cylinder. The displaced fuel is returned to the float chamber via a small hole at the upper end of the cylinder, and no delivery is made. As the throttle is released the recuperation action is repeated.

Adjustments

The quantity of fuel delivered may be adjusted by means of alternative link-rod positions on the connection to the accelerator linkage.

Economizer

The use of a slightly enriched mixture will enable an engine to develop its maximum power at any particular throttle opening. Because vehicle engines seldom require maximum power, it is now usual to reduce their fuel consumption by employing slightly weak mixtures for the more frequent part-throttle-opening conditions, and to increase the mixture strength for full-throttle conditions only, i.e. slightly enriched mixtures are not used over the whole speed range.

While the use of slightly weak mixtures under full-throttle conditions results in overheating, and the possible burning of the exhaust valves and seats, an important advantage of the petrol engine is that under part-throttle-opening conditions weak mixtures can be used with no ill effects. It is true that weak mixtures result in a slight power loss, but the maximum power is not required under these conditions and a worth-while saving of fuel can be obtained.

In the simpler types of Zenith carburettor a special device is not required for economical cruising because the fuel delivery is automatically reduced by the drop in the air speed at part-throttle openings. In the more advanced types an economizer is incorporated which operates only when the *manifold* depression is large, i.e. at part-throttle openings.

Construction

The economizer is fitted either in the top of the float chamber or on the side of the main air tube. It consists of a disc valve which is attached to a spring-loaded diaphragm influenced by *manifold* depression, and which controls the size of an air bleed between the air-cleaner end of the main air tube and the engine side of the throttle valve.

Operation

When the throttle is only part open (cruising speeds) a fairly high *manifold* depression is produced. This acts upon the spring side of the diaphragm through a small duct which connects the diaphragm chamber to the main air tube at a point below the throttle valve. The inner side of the diaphragm is influenced by atmospheric pressure via another duct system which allows a small and permanent air bleed into the top of the compensator well. The difference between these two pressures causes the diaphragm and the disc valve to move

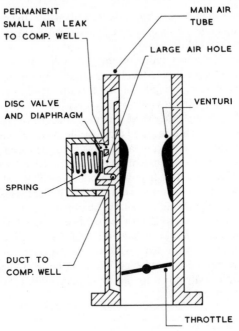

Fig. 6.8 Economizer

outward against the force of the spring – so opening the larger air hole. This allows more air to flow into the compensator well and, by reducing the pressure difference between the float chamber and the spray beak, reduces the quantity of fuel supplied by the compensator system. The mixture strength from the main and compensator system together is therefore reduced to give the economical mixture strength required for cruising.

As the throttle is opened wider, the *manifold* depression is reduced. The pressure difference between the two sides of the diaphragm is not sufficient to move the diaphragm and the disc valve against the force of the spring, and the larger air hole is closed. The air flow into the compensator well is therefore limited by the small and permanent air hole, and the action of the full pressure difference between the float chamber and the spray beak results in the main and compensator systems supplying the slightly enriched mixture needed for acceleration and maximum power.

These carburettors are of the fixed-venturi, variable-depression type. The venturi may be detachable, and the main air tube and the float chamber are a one-piece die casting. All the fuel and air jets are easily accessible.

Float chamber
Although the float chamber is not detachable, its lid, carrying the float needle and seat assembly, can be removed to expose the internally fitted air jets. A hollow metal float is used to operate the needle valve via a pivoted lever. A hollow brass plug carries the main fuel jet and is screwed into the side of the chamber above its floor or base. Another plug is used as a drain plug. In the older types the float chamber was vented directly to the atmosphere but later types are vented to the main air tube under the air cleaner.

Main spraying system
In these carburettors the spray assembly and the compensating device or system for mixture strength are combined to form a main carburettor compensated by air bleed. In principle this is similar to the compensating system of the Zenith carburettor used by itself – except that the entry of air into the compensating well is limited by an air jet. This is called the air-corrector jet, and its size controls the degree of compensation or correction, i.e, determines how much the mixture strength is reduced as the air speed is increased.

Construction
The spray assembly is arranged in the centre of the main air tube, and consists of a hollow tube supported at its lower end by a hollow strut integral with the main casting. This tube has radially disposed spray holes midway along its length, coinciding with the smallest diameter of the venturi. At the lower end of the tube a well is formed

in the strut and this is supplied with fuel via the main fuel jet in the float chamber.

Dipping into the fuel in the well is a second tube called an emulsion tube or diffuser tube. This has a series of holes at its lower end –

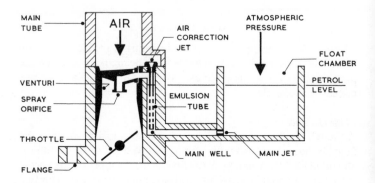

Fig. 6.9 Spray system

below the level of the spray holes – and is held in position by the air-corrector jet which is screwed into the upper end of the spray tube.

Operation

Idling. Under idling conditions, the depression in the main air tube is formed at the edges of the almost-closed throttle. Mixture must therefore be delivered to a point near the throttle edge, and this is arranged by a series of ducts in the casting. These connect the throttle edge with (a) fuel under atmospheric pressure and (b) filtered air under atmospheric pressure. The pressure difference between the fuel well in the spray assembly and the depression at the throttle edge causes fuel to flow from the well, through the fuel jet (pilot) to the throttle edge. The same pressure difference causes air to flow through the pilot jet air bleed in the pilot jet to the throttle edge. The sizes of the fuel and the air jets determines the strength of the idling mixture (about 10:1) while the *quantity* of mixture is regulated by a taper-ended screw fitted into the delivery hole or orifice. This hole is at the engine side of the throttle when the throttle is against its idling stop, and a progression hole above the throttle ensures fuel delivery as the throttle is opened.

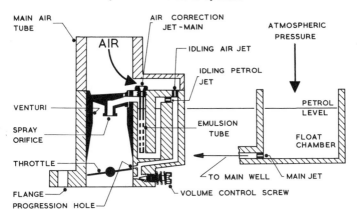

Fig. 6.10 Idling system

Low medium speeds. As the accelerator is depressed to increase the engine speed, the throttle edge passes the progression hole and the depression is reduced as the restriction to the air flow is reduced. At the same time the increased speed of the air produces an increasing depression in the venturi and this acts at the spray holes. This depression results in a pressure difference between the float chamber and the spray holes, and the fuel between the emulsion tube and the spray tube is forced to flow upwards, and out of the spray holes. This action, combined with the previous operation of the idling system, results in *some* of the holes in the emulsion tube being exposed as the fuel level falls. The pressure difference therefore causes air to flow through the air-corrector jet and the tube holes to premix or emulsify the fuel as it passes through the spray holes. Under these conditions of progressive acceleration, both the idling and the main systems are delivering fuel, and the mixture strength is being progressively reduced from the idling strength of about 10:1 to about 12:1.

Economical cruising. When the engine is operating at its lower cruising speeds, i.e. at a steady part-throttle opening, the depression in the venturi is relatively small and both fuel and air are forced through the holes in the emulsion and spray tubes. The fuel flow is controlled by the combination of the size of the jet and the difference between the fuel levels in the float chamber and the well. The air flow is determined by the size and number of holes in the emulsion exposed by the fuel. As higher cruising speeds are reached, the increased venturi depression increases the pressure difference, causing the flow of both fuel and air. The fuel flow is limited by the action of the jet, but the air flow is increased as more of the holes in the emulsion tube are exposed by the falling level of fuel in the well. The resulting mixture strength is therefore reduced to between 15:1 and 17:1 and the mixture is emulsified to a greater degree.

Full power. To obtain full power, a richer mixture (about 12:1) must be supplied, and the necessary enrichment is obtained through the action of the air-corrector jet. When the throttle is opened fully, after the higher cruising speeds, the venturi depression and its associated pressure difference are increased to their maximum values. The fuel delivery is still being limited by the action of the fuel jet and at this point the air-corrector jet limits the flow of air through the emulsion tube. The system therefore acts in a similar manner to the simple carburettor at high air speeds, the mixture strength being increased as the density of the air is reduced by its acceleration through the venturi.

Starting device

This may be either an auxiliary carburettor or a strangler valve similar to that already described in the section on the Zenith carburettor. The auxiliary carburettors may be classified as semi- or fully-automatic types according to whether or not they automatically reduce the mixture strength when the engine fires and runs.

Bi-starter

This is a semi-automatic starting device which has a two-position manual control. The device consists of a petrol jet and well, an air jet, a mixing or valve chamber, and a set of connecting ducts.

The petrol jet and well of the starter are arranged in the wall of the float chamber, the well being open to atmospheric pressure (filtered air) and the jet restricting the flow of petrol into the well. The mixing chamber is cylindrical in shape and is connected by ducts to (a) the top of the main air tube, (b) the petrol well and (c) the main air tube at the engine side of the throttle valve.

The starter jet controls the flow of filtered air into the valve chamber from the top of the main air tube. The entry of petrol into the chamber, and the exit of mixture from it, are controlled by a disc

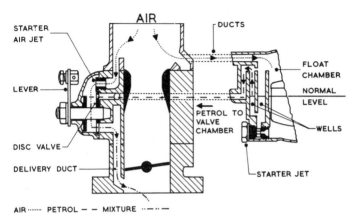

Fig. 6.11 Bi-starter

valve which is turned by the control lever. This valve is pierced by holes which coincide with the ducts according to the position of the control lever. A large or a small hole can coincide with the petrol supply duct, while the mixture exit duct may be opened by alternative holes of the same size, or be sealed off by the disc. The location of the holes in relation to the ducts is made exact by the action of a spring which forces a ball into notches cut in the edge of a second disc, this disc turning with the valve disc and lever.

Cold starting (full choke)
When the engine is cold the choke control is pulled fully open, so turning the disc valve to open the mixture exit duct and aligning the *larger* petrol hole with the petrol supply duct. The accelerator pedal is not depressed when starting.

As the starter motor is operated, a depression is produced in the manifold (because the throttle is closed) and this depression is communicated to the valve chamber. A pressure difference is therefore produced between the manifold and (a) the upper end of the main air tube and (b) the float chamber. This results in air being forced through the chamber via the petrol hole in the disc valve. The mixture is then forced into the manifold below the closed throttle valve via the mixture exit hole in the valve. The mixture strength under these conditions is about 4:1.

Cold running (half choke)

When the engine fires and runs, the increased speed of the pistons increases the depression in the *manifold*. This would result in an increased pressure difference and an unwanted increase in the mixture strength, so the control lever and disc valve are returned to the half-open position. This brings the *smaller* petrol hole of the valve into alignment with the petrol supply duct and, because the air jet size remains the same, the mixture strength is reduced to between 6:1 and 8:1 as required for cold running. The throttle may be opened slightly to give a faster idle. The engine can be run safely on this strength of mixture until it has warmed up sufficiently to run on the normal idling mixture of about 10:1. When the normal operating temperatures are reached, the control lever is returned to the fully-off position, the disc valve then seals off the mixture exit duct and the petrol supply duct.

NOTE. This starter device bypasses the main carburettor and is operated by *manifold* depression.

Self-starter

This is an automatic starting device in which the control lever has no mid-way position. In construction it is very similar to the Bi-starter, but the disc valve has only one hole for petrol supply and the petrol well system is similar to the Zenith compensating system.

Cold starting (full choke)

The action of this system is the same as that of the Bi-starter, the mixture strength being about 4:1.

Cold running (full choke)

When the engine fires and runs, the much increased *manifold* depression causes a greater pressure difference and the petrol wells are quickly emptied. As the first well is open to atmospheric pressure, it now becomes an air bleed and reduces the pressure difference between the float chamber and the valve or mixing chamber. At the same time the petrol jet is limiting the flow of petrol and the air jet is unchanged in size. The combination of these actions automatically reduces the mixture strength, to between 6:1 and 8:1, as the engine fires and runs. When the engine has reached its normal running temperature the control is returned to the fully-off position.

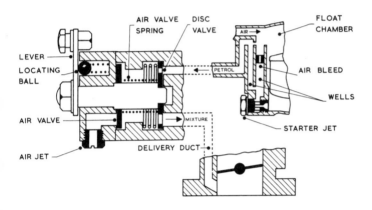

Fig. 6.12 Zero starter

Autostarter

Some of the later Solex carburettors have a starting device in which the control itself is operated by a temperature-sensitive bi-metallic coil, i.e. the driver does not operate the choke control. In these devices one end of the bi-metallic coil is anchored to its air-tight casing, while the other end is attached to the spindle of the disc valve. The casing is secured to the chamber of the disc valve and air can pass between them. A U-shaped metal tube is arranged in the exhaust manifold, and the pressure difference between the inlet manifold and the upper air tube forces air to flow through this tube and the coil and valve chambers. The petrol supply duct has a small outlet port which is always open and a larger port which may be varied in size by a depression-operated, spring-loaded piston.

When the engine is cold, the contraction of the coil turns the disc valve to allow the manifold depression to influence the coil and valve chambers. The pressure difference forces air to flow through the heating tube and the chambers. The piston spring forces the piston to fully expose the larger petrol port and the 4:1 cold-start mixture is delivered.

When the engine fires and runs, the increased pressure difference causes the piston to move against the action of its spring and close off the larger port. As the air flow is increased while the fuel flow is reduced, the mixture strength is automatically reduced to the 6:1 to 8:1 strength required.

As the air flowing is gradually heated by the exhaust gases, the bi-metallic coil is caused to expand, progressively turning the disc valve to seal off the air exit duct and so to put the starter device out of action.

Accelerator pump
Construction

This consists of a small chamber which has one wall in the form of a flexible diaphragm. The diaphragm is forced outward by a coil

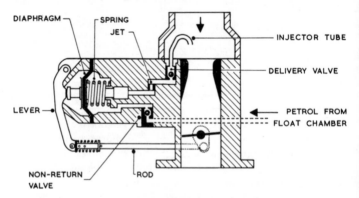

Fig. 6.13 Accelerator pump

spring and inward by a lever attached to the throttle linkage. The pump chamber and the float chamber are connected by an intake duct in which is fitted a ball type of non-return valve. The delivery duct passes from the pump chamber to an injector tube arranged

with its outlet near the upper end of the main spraying assembly.
A metering jet and a non-return valve are fitted in this duct.

Delivery
When the accelerator pedal is depressed, the lever forces the diaphragm inward and so reduces the chamber volume. The pressure is
increased and so forces the intake ball valve down harder to its seat.
At the same time the delivery ball valve is forced from its seat and
petrol passes out into the main air tube via the metering jet and the
injector tube. As delivery is completed, the delivery ball valve falls
back on to its seat.

Recuperation
When the throttle is released, the diaphragm spring forces the diaphragm outwards, increasing the chamber volume and reducing its
pressure. The pressure difference between the pump chamber and
the float chamber opens the intake valve and forces petrol to flow
into, and fill, the pump chamber. As the chamber fills, the pressures
equalize and the intake ball valve falls back upon its seat.

Econostat
This device is incorporated in certain Solex carburettors intended
for use with four-cylinder engines. It is a device for full-power enrichment which enables weaker and more economical mixtures to
be used at part-throttle openings.

In these carburettors the spray-tube assembly is arranged in the
wall of the main air tube, the spray holes being situated at the inner
end of a large duct which communicates with the centre of the
venturi. The Econostat petrol jet is at the foot of a petrol well in the
wall of the float chamber and the air jet is at the top of the well. A
duct in the casting connects the spray holes to a point in the well just
below the air jet.

When the throttle is fully opened to obtain full power, the pressure difference between the spray holes and the float chamber is
large enough to force the petrol in the well to flow upward and out
to the spray holes. At the same time air is forced through the air
jet and the resulting mixture is *added* to the normal delivery of the
main spraying system. The size of the Econostat air jet determines
when the Econostat comes into operation, and the size of its petrol

jet determines the degree of enrichment provided for full-power conditions.

Under part-throttle operating conditions the air flow through the Econostat air jet is such that the pressure difference between the spray holes and float chamber is not sufficient to force petrol to flow up to the top of the well – and so no delivery is made to supplement the normal delivery from the main spraying system. The petrol and air jet sizes of this system can therefore be selected to provide maximum fuel economy at part-throttle openings, and to avoid excessive mixture strengths at full-throttle low-speed operating.

In a number of Solex carburettors, economy devices are combined with mechanical or depression-operated accelerator pumps.

THE SU CARBURETTOR

In these types the venturi size is varied automatically by the degree of throttle opening and the load against which the engine is working. The variation of the size of the venturi results in the air speed over the jet being approximately constant, and therefore the pressure difference between the jet and the float chamber is approximately constant. It also results in one jet being adequate for the whole speed range of the engine.

The fact that the venturi size alters to maintain a constant depression necessitates the variation of the effective size of the petrol jet, in order to obtain the varying strengths of mixture required under different operating conditions. These carburettors are known as constant-vacuum (depression) or variable-choke (venturi) types.

Construction

The unit consists of a main air tube with a disc-type throttle valve. a float chamber, a tubular petrol jet, a tapered needle attached to a piston, and a dome or chamber which encloses the piston.

The throttle valve is arranged at the engine end of the main air tube, with its axis or spindle parallel with the axis of the intake manifold. An adjustable, low-speed, throttle stop is provided. The float chamber is arranged forward of the air tube and is secured to it by a bolt. In the H types this bolt is hollow and forms a part of the duct through which petrol is forced from the float chamber to the jet. In the HS types the duct is replaced by a nylon pipe.

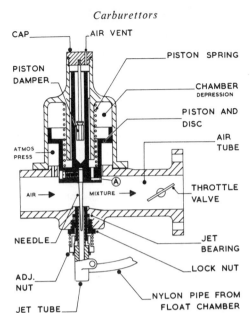

Fig. 6.14 SU layout

The piston and its enclosing dome are arranged at right angles to the air tube, and above it, and the dome is secured by screws. The hollow piston rod or guide is an accurate fit in a bore formed in the centre of the dome. The piston has an integral suction disc, and is

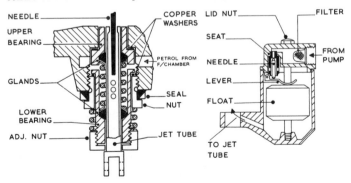

Fig. 6.15 Detail of H type

forced down by the combination of its weight and the action of a light coil spring. The piston forms one side of the venturi and the jet needle is secured into its under face by a small screw. Two small stop pins are also fitted into this under face to ensure that air can still enter the engine when the piston is fully down, i.e. when the engine is started. The space in the dome above the piston suction disc is influenced by the depression in the air tube through a small hole (A) in the engine side of the lower part of the piston. The space below the suction disc is permanently influenced by atmospheric pressure.

The jet tube is arranged immediately below the piston and the needle in such a way that the needle is always dipping into the jet. The height of the jet can be adjusted by a nut, and this is used to adjust the mixture strength under warm idling conditions. The floor

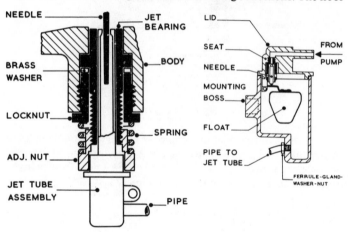

Fig. 6.16 Detail of HS type

of the air tube is raised slightly under the piston to form the jet bridge. This helps the rush of air to atomize the liquid fuel adequately under all operating conditions. In the H types the jet tube is sealed into the jet tube petrol chamber by cork or plastic seals which are spring loaded. In the HS types this sealing is avoided by the use of the external feed pipe of nylon. In both types the jet can be lowered in relation to the needle to provide the very rich mixtures needed for cold starting.

The needle has so many slightly different diameters that its pro-file becomes a tapering curve which determines the economy and power output of a given engine (as far as carburation is concerned). The taper is very carefully calculated and it is then checked by a large number of practical tests, different curves being required for different designs of engine. It is most important that only the recom-mended needle be fitted to a particular carburettor and engine com-bination. The taper of the needle is also such that when the mixture strength for warm idling has been correctly adjusted the correct mixture strengths will be provided automatically over the remainder of the speed and load range.

Operation

At a given throttle opening, and under a given engine speed and load combination, the depression formed in the air tube is communicated to the space above the piston suction disc. As the space below the disc is under atmospheric pressure the pressure difference causes the piston and needle to lift – until a position is reached where the force due to the pressure difference is equalled by the combined forces due to the mass of the piston and the force of its spring. At this point the effective diameter of the jet is permitting the flow of the correct mass of petrol to suit the weight of air entering the engine. The taper of the needle is such that for every possible position of the piston (venturi size) there is an equivalent jet area which will provide the correct strength of mixture for that piston position.

NOTE. The degree of piston lift is determined by the *quantity* of mixture flowing into the engine, i.e. is determined by the combina-tion of throttle position, engine load and engine speed.

The depression over the jet remains almost constant, and it is designed to be such that (a) the liquid petrol is adequately atomized at all air speeds and (b) the restriction of the air flow does not prevent the development of full power.

Cold starting. The very rich mixtures of about 4:1 required for cold starting are obtained by (a) increasing the size of the petrol jet and (b) reducing the size of the air intake. The effective size of the jet is increased by the operation of the choke control; this lowers the jet in relation to the needle and at the same time opens the throttle to its fast, cold idling position. When the engine is not running, i.e.

when there is no air flow, the passage through the main air tube is restricted to the very small gap between the under face of the piston and the jet bridge. The minimum gap is determined by the piston stop pins which contact the bridge. When the starter motor is operated, the movements of the engine pistons produce a depression in the intake *manifold* which is communicated, via the partly-open throttle valve, to the main air tube. The pressure difference forces air to flow under the piston into the engine, and petrol to flow from the float chamber to the jet bridge. Here the petrol is atomized by, and mixed with, the air flow, to form the rich cold-starting mixture. The moment air flows into the engine the depression created in the *venturi* is communicated to the space above the piston suction disc. The resulting pressure difference between the two sides of the disc causes the piston and needle to lift slightly to provide the slightly greater *quantity* of rich mixture required.

Cold running. When the engine fires and runs, the increased speed of the air through the venturi increases the depression, which in turn results in the further lifting of the piston and needle. More mixture is provided, but its strength can now be reduced to the 6–8:1 required for cold, fast idling by slightly easing off the choke control.

Warm idling. As the engine reaches its normal operating temperatures, the choke control must be returned to the fully-off position. This results in the throttle valve being closed to its normal idling stop, and in the jet tube being returned to its normal height in relation to the level of fuel in the float chamber. The reduction of the jet size while the air supply remains almost constant results in the weakening of the mixture to the 10:1 required for normal idling. The constant depression results in a high air speed across the jet, even under idling conditions, and in a *separate* supply system not being required for idling mixture.

Acceleration. A slightly enriched mixture of about 12:1 is needed for acceleration. This is obtained naturally in the SU carburettor because there is always a short delay or lag between the acceleration of the air stream and the corresponding lift of the piston and needle. The delay momentarily increases the depression over the jet and the rich mixture is momentarily supplied. This is normally sufficient for a steady acceleration of the engine.

The delay may be slightly increased by the use of a piston damper, causing a slightly longer flow of rich mixture which makes rapid acceleration of the engine possible.

The piston of the damper is fitted into the hollow piston rod and incorporates a one-way valve. This operates in SAE 20 oil and is so designed that, although it will not impede the downward motion of the piston, it will slightly delay its lift.

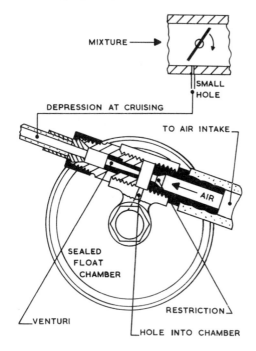

Fig. 6.17 Economizer

Economical cruising. When SU carburettors are used with certain engines the fuel economy can be improved, under part-throttle and light-load conditions, by the use of a small device attached to the lid of the float chamber.

The device is essentially a controlled air bleed into the float chamber. A small pipe connects the top of the float chamber to a small hole near the throttle edge, a small venturi being arranged between the two. Apart from this air pipe, the *float chamber is sealed*.

When the throttle is almost closed, the hole is at the carburettor piston side of the throttle and only the small *air tube depression* is communicated to the float chamber. Similarly only a small depression is communicated when the throttle is fully opened because the *manifold depression* is very small. In these two situations the normal pressure difference between the float chamber and the jet bridge is maintained.

When the throttle is between the closed and fully-open positions, the fairly large depression in the air tube is communicated to the float chamber. This reduced the pressure difference and therefore the quantity of fuel delivered – but the air supply is unchanged. The mixture strength is therefore reduced and a worth while saving of fuel is made. The venturi in the device acts to limit the maximum depression communicated to limit the weakening-off effect to about 15:1 to 16:1.

The SU starter carburettor
This is a separate starting carburettor attached to the fuel inlet base of the sealed-adjustment type of main carburettor. Its operation is controlled by either the ignition switch and a thermostatic switch, or by a manually operated switch.

Construction
The unit consists of a solenoid-operated, ball-jointed and spring-loaded disc valve which controls the communication of the depression in the intake manifold to a vertical chamber. Inside the chamber is an integral plunger and a needle valve which is lifted to its highest position by the action of a spring. The lower end of the needle is tapered and dips into, but does not close off, a petrol jet supplied from the float chamber of the main carburettor. The upper end of the plunger passes through an adjusting nut at the top of the chamber and has an integral shoulder at the end which limits the downward motion of the plunger. A vertical air passage, which is open to atmospheric pressure, is arranged parallel to the needle chamber.

Operation
When the engine is cold and the control switch allows current to

flow through the solenoid, the disc valve is opened by the electro-magnetic action of the solenoid. The depression in the intake manifold at cranking speed is communicated to the needle chamber, and the pressure difference between the chamber and the float

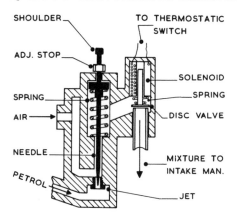

Fig. 6.18 Thermostatic choke

chamber forces petrol to flow through the jet. At the same time air is forced through the chamber and the resulting mixture is forced up, and out into the intake manifold, to provide the very rich mixture needed for cold starting. The strength of this mixture is adjusted by the needle adjusting nut.

When the engine fires and runs, the depression in the intake manifold is greatly increased by the increased speed of the engine pistons. This should result in an even richer mixture but because this depression acts in the needle chamber the pressure difference is now large enough to overcome the force due to the needle spring – and the needle is forced down further into the jet. The fuel flow is therefore reduced while the air flow is increasing and the resulting mixture strength is reduced to the 6–8:1 needed for cold running.

When the throttle is opened the depression in the intake manifold is automatically reduced and the needle spring lifts the needle in proportion to the reduction. This provides a rich mixture which is additional to the supply from the main carburettor and which enables the car to be driven off while the engine is still cold.

As the engine reaches its normal running temperature, the solenoid is switched out of action by either the thermostatic or the manual switch, and the disc valve is closed by its spring. This seals off the manifold and prevents the depression acting in the needle chamber – so putting the starter carburettor out of action.

7

The Cooling System

Conditions

In all types of vehicle engine the power is derived from the expansion of air. The necessary heat is obtained by the burning of the fuel in the air, and this produces temperatures which are higher than the melting-points of the engine materials. Cast iron melts at about 1200 °C and aluminium alloy at about 650 °C, while the temperature of the burning petrol may be as high as 2000 °C. It is therefore most important that excessive heat be removed quickly and continuously to avoid damage to the engine.

For the engine to operate efficiently, it must be kept within a certain range of temperatures. The normal range for water-cooled engines is from 77 °C to 85 °C; air-cooled engines run slightly hotter.

If the running temperatures are too high, the excessive heat will cause too much expansion in the pistons, and the crankshaft journals, and these may seize into their bearings. The oil will break down chemically into gums and resins, and so be made useless for its work as a lubricant and coolant. Pre-ignition may be caused by local overheating of the exhaust valve seats and spark plugs. A loss of power will be caused if the fresh charge of mixture is overheated. In water-cooled engines the water may boil and produce steam pressures high enough to burst the rubber pipes and to blow out the core plugs.

If the running temperatures are too low, the petrol will not be fully vaporized and liquid petrol will wash the lubricating oil from the cylinder walls and dilute the oil in the sump. This will lead to high fuel consumption, the formation of heavy deposits of carbon in the combustion chamber, and a faster rate of piston, ring, and bore wear. The crankshaft bearings may also be damaged by the thinner oil and the carbon particles swept around in it. The temperature range from 77 °C to 85 °C allows a safety margin up to 98 °C for low-gear work such as hill climbing and driving in heavy traffic.

Heat dissipation

The *total* amount of heat energy released by the combustion of the petrol is dissipated in the following ways:

Converted into mechanical energy	Useful	25%
Passed out in exhaust gases	Wasted	40%
Passed out through cooling system	Wasted	28%
Passed out through lubrication system	Wasted	7%

Note that only one quarter, approximately, of each litre of petrol supplies useful work, that is, the thermal efficiency of the petrol engine is only about 25%. The compression-ignition engine is a little better in its conversion of heat energy into mechanical energy, its thermal efficiency being about 40%.

Two main cooling systems are used in vehicle engines. The air-cooled systems use air as their cooling medium and water-cooled systems use air and water.

AIR COOLING

This type is used more frequently in motor-cycle and aircraft engines, although a few car engines are cooled by air. Some stationary engines are air cooled also, usually by means of a driven fan. Air cooling is not often used for multi-cylinder engines because it is difficult to cool all the cylinders equally, and the control of temperature is not very accurate. A rather complicated system of baffles is often needed and these are vulnerable to dirt and damage.

In air-cooled systems the cylinders and heads are heavily finned to increase the heat-dissipating areas. Aluminium alloys are used wherever possible because these are better heat conductors than irons and steels. Air-cooled engines run at higher temperatures than water-cooled engines so their bearing clearances must be larger. Due to the absence of sound-baffling water jackets they are usually more noisy in operation.

A simplified example of a controlled air-cooling system is shown in Fig. 7.2. The cylinders are enclosed by a sheet-metal housing through which the air flows. The inlet is varied in size by a shutter controlled, through a system of levers, by a thermostat fitted inside the housing. An engine-driven fan maintains the air flow under all conditions.

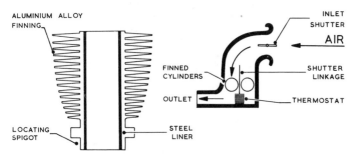

Fig. 7.1 Air cooling   Fig. 7.2 Controlled air cooling

WATER COOLING

Water is a better conductor of heat than air, so in these systems water is used to extract the heat from the metal surrounding the combustion chambers and valve ports. The heat is then removed from the water by a stream of air and the cooled water returned to the heated areas of metal. There are three different water-cooling systems:

(1) The thermo-syphon system, which is now seldom used.
(2) The impeller-assisted thermo-syphon system, which is used in the engines of most cars and light commercial vehicles.
(3) The pump system used for larger engines.

In the simple thermo-syphon system, circulation of the water depends solely upon the fact that when water is heated it becomes less dense and rises. Its place is taken by cooler and more dense water which is then heated and rises to be replaced by the cooled water previously heated. In this way a slow circulation is obtained by *convection* currents.

Disadvantages of the simple system are that:

(a) the circulation depends upon convection currents and is therefore slow;
(b) a large volume and mass of water must be carried due to the slow circulation;

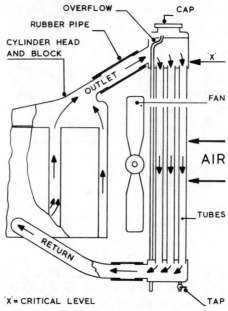

Fig. 7.3 Thermo-syphon system

(c) large-bore pipes must be used to offer as little restriction to the flow as possible;

(d) the radiator tanks must be above and below the water jacket, and this restricts the body designer because the radiator must be long and vertical;

(e) the water level is critical in that if it is allowed to fall below the level of the floor of the top tank the circulation is stopped and boiling will occur.

Because of these disadvantages, this system has been replaced by the impeller-assisted thermo-syphon system, and the pressurized system. All modern water-cooled systems have a radiator, a thermostat and some form of pump.

The Radiator
Function
The radiator is designed to expose to the air stream as large a cooling

area as possible in as small a frontal area as possible. It also acts as a tank for some of the water carried.

Construction

The usual form of construction is that of sheet-steel or brass pressings which are formed into top and bottom tanks. These are connected by brass or copper tubes fitted with finning to increase their surface areas. The block of tubes is sometimes termed the core, and in the radiators of cars and the lighter commercial vehicles the core may be of the tubular or of the film type.

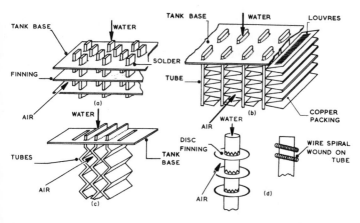

Fig. 7.4 Radiator construction: (a) tube type; (b) gill tube type; (c) film type; (d) commercial type

Tubular core. This is composed of thin-walled copper or brass tubes arranged in staggered rows. The tubes may be of round, oval or rectangular cross-section and all pass through a series of thin brass plates which act as finning and increase the area through which heat can be dissipated. The highest and lowest of these plates act as the floor of the top tank and the top of the bottom tanks respectively.
Gill tube core. This is similar to the tubular core but the construction is simpler.
Film core. The tubes in this core are made from thin brass stampings and extend over the full thickness of the core. They are bent to form square spaces for the air passages through the core. The effect of

this is that longer tubes can be fitted into a given radiator height to increase the cooling area.

Heavy commercial core. The core is much stronger, and the tanks are made from two aluminium-alloy castings which are bolted together. The tubes are circular in cross-section and have thicker walls. They are fitted into the tanks individually and are made watertight by rubber and metal seals. Each is finned by either copper discs or by a spiral of copper wire.

Radiators may be repaired by the use of a soft (low temperature) solder but great care must be taken to avoid using too much heat. Generally, it is better to leave core repairs to the specialist tradesman, but the commercial types may be repaired by splitting the tanks and replacing any damaged tubes.

In all these core designs the water flows down the tubes while the air flows around them. Horizontal, or cross flow, types are also used, and these employ a separate header tank.

Radiators must have a filler cap and an overflow or vent pipe, and often have a drain tap fitted to the bottom tank.

The thermostat (bellows type)

Function

The thermostat is used to control the flow of water through the radiator. When the engine is cold it prevents water leaving the water

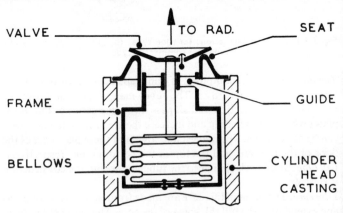

Fig. 7.5 Thermostat: bellows type

jacket; when the engine is hot it allows water to pass from the water jacket and through the radiator at a rate sufficient to keep the water temperature within the 77 °C–85 °C range. In some vehicles a thermostat is used to regulate the flow of *air* through the radiator. This it does by controlling a valve in a pressurized oil system; this valve in turn, by means of piston and cylinder-operated levers, opens and closes a set of shutters, in the front of the radiator.

Construction

The unit is composed of a disc valve and seat, and is fitted between the cylinder head and the radiator top tank. The valve is attached to the top of a stack of thin brass capsules arranged to form a bellows. These are filled with a volatile liquid such as acetone or methyl alcohol, and the bellows is secured to the frame and suspended from the seat.

Operation

Engine cold. Under cold conditions, the valve is held closed down to its seat by the contraction of the bellows, and no water can pass from the cylinder head to the radiator.

Engine hot. As the water in the jacket is heated, the volatile liquid in the bellows is converted into a vapour. This causes each bellows to expand and the total expansion lifts the valve from its seat. The water can now flow from the cylinder head to be cooled in the radiator, that is, circulation is started. When the engine is switched off the valve is pulled down to its seat, by the contraction of the bellows as the vaporized alcohol is converted into a liquid by the lower temperatures, until it is fully closed when the temperature has fallen below 77 °C.

The wax thermostat

Construction

This type has a much stronger action than the bellows type and is less likely to fail in service. It is not affected by the pressure in the system and it is therefore used in pressurized systems – where pressures of more than about 48 kN/m^2 are employed. The valve is opened by the force produced by the relatively large expansion of a special wax as it changes from a solid to a liquid state.

The valve is arranged below the seat and is forced towards the seat by a strong spring. A bridge over the seat and the mounting flange has a taper-ended thrust pin attached to it and the lower end of this pin is surrounded by a cylindrical rubber sleeve itself surrounded by wax. The wax and the sleeve are both enclosed by, and sealed into, a very strong metal capsule to which the valve is attached. The lower part of the capsule and the lower end of the spring are supported by a frame secured to the mounting flange.

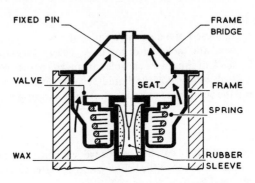

Fig. 7.6 Thermostat: wax type

Operation
Cold. When the water in the engine is cold, the wax has its least volume and the valve is forced up to its seat by the spring. No water can pass from the engine into the radiator.
Hot. As the water in the engine absorbs heat, the wax begins to melt and in so doing expands. Because of the construction of the capsule, the powerful expansion force of the wax is directed into compressing the rubber and so forcing the thrust pin upwards out of the capsule. As the pin is attached to the bridge and cannot move, the capsule and the attached valve are forced to move down from the seat, so opening the valve (see Fig. 7.6).

Failure of this type is usually due to the rubber sleeve being damaged by either age or mechanical means. If the rubber of the sleeve loses its sensitivity the valve will not be opened until higher than normal temperatures are reached. If the sleeve is punctured below the pin the valve will remain open. Other damage may cause the valve to remain closed.

Hoses

The rubber hoses used in the cooling system must be fairly resistant to heat and oil. They must also be fairly strong mechanically. Hoses are usually moulded into their correct shape, and are either fabric reinforced or thick walled. Those used in pressurized cooling systems operating under higher pressures between about 48 kN/m² and 100 kN/m² must have extra reinforcement.

It is important that hoses be examined at regular intervals and kept clean and in good condition. Dry and cracking hoses, and oil-soaked and spongy hoses, must be replaced.

Fans

Function

The fan is used to draw air through the radiator core. Early cooling systems had very large radiators which provided adequate cooling when the vehicle was stationary, and when the rather small and slow-running engine was being worked hard; when the vehicle was travelling normally the air flow through the radiator tended to over-cool the engine and a fan was not needed.

As engine speed and power is increased the cooling system has more work to do and it has therefore to be made more efficient, i.e. less bulk and weight of water must do more cooling. The fitting of an engine-driven fan makes possible the use of less water and smaller radiators, and still provides adequate cooling at low or zero vehicle speeds.

Construction

The fan in the simple thermo-syphon system is a two-bladed pro-pellor bolted to a pulley and driven by the crankshaft pulley through some form of belt; in some engines the fan was attached to the dynamo pulley. In most modern systems the fan is bolted to the impeller-pump pulley and fans with two, four, or six blades are used. The radiator core may be shrouded to make the fan more efficient.

The real value of the fan is at low vehicle speeds and at maximum engine speeds. During most open-road operation the fan is not really required and the power absorbed in driving it is wasted, so increasing the fuel consumption. These losses of power and fuel can be reduced by a device which enables the fan to be operated only when it is really needed. In one such device the fan is driven by an electric motor, the operation of which is controlled by a temperature-sensitive switch. In another device the drive to the fan is made through a fluid coupling, the fluid flow being controlled by a temperature sensitive valve. In both devices it is the temperature of the cooling water which determines whether or not the fan is driven.

The impeller pump

Function

The impeller pump is bolted to the front or side of the engine, and is used to speed up the circulation of the water through the system. This makes possible the carrying of less volume and mass of water; the use of a smaller and lighter radiator (the position of which is not critical), and the directing of the coolest water to the most heated areas.

Construction

The pump consists of an impeller in the form of a disc with integral tapered blades on one side. The blades may be straight or curved, according to the degree of centrifugal force required, and are deeper at the impeller centre. The impeller is secured to one end of a shaft carried in a pre-packed and grease-sealed bearing. The other end of the shaft carries the drive pulley and the fan, and is driven by a vee belt from the crankshaft. The shaft assembly is mounted in a cast-iron casing which also surrounds the impeller, the bearings being protected from the water by a spring-loaded carbon sealing ring. The water inlet from the bottom tank of the radiator leads into the centre of the impeller, and an outlet from a point at the edge of the impeller directs the water into the distributor tube in the cylinder head.

Operation

The impeller is rotated as the engine starts and the water at its centre is impelled along the blades by the action of centrifugal force. The water is then thrown off the edge of the impeller and directed to the outlet by the casing. The centre of the impeller (low pressure) is refilled with the water displaced from the radiator and the circulation continues for as long as the impeller is rotated. Should the

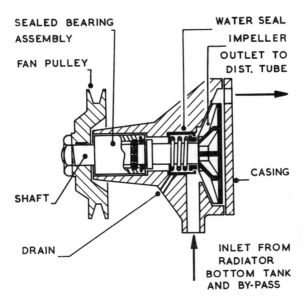

Fig. 7.7 Impeller pump

thermostat valve be closed, the water leaving the pump is returned to the pump inlet through an internal or an external by-pass.

The pumps used by the larger engines make use of a greater centrifugal force and the resulting circulation is much faster. These types are larger and more strongly constructed, and are therefore driven by the timing gears or from the camshaft.

The impeller-assisted system
Construction
This is similar to that of the simpler system but a wider and lower radiator is used, and a thermostat, a water distributor tube and an engine-driven impeller pump are added. The pump circulates the

water at a higher speed and much more positively than the convection currents of the simpler system, but a pressure is not built up by the pump. The thermostat is a temperature-controlled valve which is fitted into the water outlet from the cylinder head and which, by controlling the amount of cooling being done by the radiator, keeps

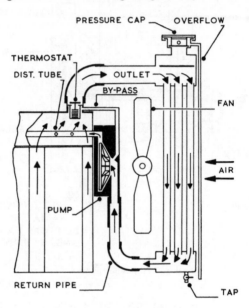

Fig. 7.8 Impeller-assisted system

the engine operating in its correct temperature range. The distributor tube is secured into the cylinder head and is perforated at certain points to direct the cooled water from the pump to the hottest parts of the cylinder head.

Operation
Engine hot. In this system the impeller pump draws cooled water from the bottom tank of the radiator and passes it into the distributor tube. The tube directs cooled water through its perforations on to the hottest areas of metal surrounding the combustion chambers and the exhaust ports. The cooled water absorbs most of the

heat and passes up around the open valve of the thermostat and out of the cylinder head to the top tank of the radiator. As the heated water passes down the radiator core, the absorbed heat is removed by the air stream through the core, and the now cooled water is drawn into the impeller pump to be recirculated.

Engine cold. The circulation starts as soon as the engine is started, so the warming time would be unduly long if it were not for the action of the thermostat. Under cold conditions, this valve is closed, and the pump is only allowed to circulate the water in the cylinder head and block. This is made possible by the use of a by-pass, either internal or external, from the low-pressure side of the impeller to a point just below the valve seat of the thermostat.

As the water absorbs heat its temperature rises, and at about 77 °C the thermostat valve begins to open to allow water to pass into the radiator and be cooled. This valve will open to positions related to the air temperature, the vehicle speed, and the load on the engine. In this manner the engine is kept within the temperature range at which it operates best, and under cold conditions need have only the same warm-up time as engines with the simple system.

Advantages

The advantages of this system over the simple system are:
(a) The positive circulation is faster, so less weight and bulk of water are needed.
(b) A smaller and lighter radiator can be used, and its position in relation to the water jacket is not so limited.
(c) Smaller bore pipes may be used.
(d) The water level is not so critical because the circulation does not depend upon convection currents.
(e) Control of the engine-operating temperature is more accurate.

Although this system is more complicated and more expensive to produce and to maintain, its use is justified by greater efficiency and by more freedom for body designers and stylists.

The pressurized system

When an engine with impeller-assisted cooling system is worked hard there is a danger that pockets of steam may be formed in the complicated shape of the cylinder-head water jacket. Steam is a very poor conductor of heat and overheating may occur at these points.

This will lead to pre-ignition and a loss of power, so this danger is reduced by using a special design of radiator neck and cap.

A pressurized system is essential for vehicles which are to be operated at very high altitudes. At an altitude of about 2100 m above sea level the boiling-point of water is about 95 °C; this is due to the fact that at this altitude the atmospheric pressure is reduced to about 83 kN/m². The losses of water under these conditions would be so great that the cooling system is suitably pressurized to prevent the formation of steam.

The pressure cap
Construction
This cap has the usual seating in the tank neck, and also includes two extra valves which are opposed to each other. The larger spring-loaded valve prevents the release of pressure from the system until

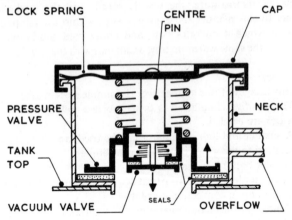

Fig. 7.9 Pressure cap: open valve type

a pressure of 28 kN/m² to 48 kN/m² is exceeded (in some systems pressures up to 100 kN/m² are used). This means that the system normally operates under pressure and this prevents the water boiling and forming steam until the temperature is above the normal boiling-point. The engine may therefore be safely operated at a temperature higher than normal. It will also develop a little more power.

Operation

When the engine is running normally the excessive pressures, together with some steam or water, are released by the lifting of the large valve against the action of its spring. The water so released escapes down the overflow pipe.

As the engine is allowed to cool down after use the small losses result in the formation of a partial vacuum in the system. This is relieved by the opening of the smaller valve when the difference between the internal pressure and that of outside atmosphere exceeds 7 kN/m². This allows air to enter the system through the overflow pipe, the valve being closed by its spring as the pressures equalize.

NOTE. The cap and the neck of the top tank are so designed that the pressure, when the engine is hot, may be released *before* the cap is completely free from the neck. This is done to reduce the possibility of boiling water being blown up into the face of the person removing the cap. The cap should only be part turned and then held until the hissing of the escaping pressure has ceased. The cap may then be released in safety.

The sealed system

In all the systems previously described the expansion of the water and air in the system results in small losses of water through the radiator overflow pipe. Over a period of operation the level may fall enough to stop the correct circulation, and so the level of water in the radiator must be checked and topped up at fairly frequent intervals. This service operation is avoided or reduced by the use of a sealed system. In its simplest form this consists of immersing the end of the overflow pipe in a quantity of water contained in a small metal or plastic bottle. It is important that the end of the pipe be prevented from rising above the surface of the water in the bottle.

As the engine reaches its normal running temperature, a pressure is built up inside the system and this, or the expansion of the water and air, forces a small quantity of water, air and steam to be discharged into the water in the bottle.

As the engine cools, the pressure in the system falls below that of the atmosphere acting upon the water in the bottle, and the pressure difference forces water from the bottle back into the system. This action continues until the pressures equalize and the vacuum valve is closed by its spring.

The pumped system
This is very much like the impeller-assisted system except that a true centrifugal pump is used. This produces a much faster circulation, so that very large engines can be cooled adequately without carrying an excessive weight of water. These pumps are usually gear-driven from the camshaft or timing gears, and may be bolted to the side of the engine.

TEMPERATURE GAUGES

These are used to indicate the temperature of the water in the engine at all times, so enabling the driver to stop the engine before over-heating can cause serious damage.
(a) The mechanical or vapour-pressure type.
(b) The electrical type.

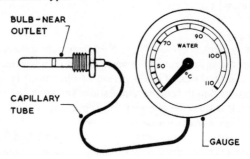

Fig. 7.10 Temperature gauge: mechanical or vapour-pressure type

Mechanical types
In these a gauge is mounted on the instrument panel and is permanently connected by a fine-bore (capillary) tube to a temperature-sensitive bulb or capsule. This is fitted into the cylinder head near the water outlet. The gauge is a sensitive type of Bourdon-tube instrument similar in construction to the oil-pressure gauge. The gauge tube and bulb are filled completely with a volatile liquid.

As the bulb is heated by the cooling water the liquid in it changes into a vapour which exerts pressure inside the gauge. The gauge converts this pressure into a reading of temperature.

The tubing must be kept away from the exhaust system and there must be no sharp bends. There must be three coils of not less than three inches diameter formed in the tubing near the gauge and near the bulb. *No attempt must be made to disconnect the tubing* because damage to this renders the whole system inoperative. If the connection between the bulb and the gauge is broken all three parts of the system must be replaced as an assembly.

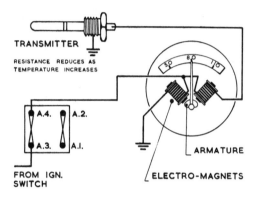

Fig. 7.11 Temperature gauge: electrical type

Electrical types

A number of different systems are in use but they all include a panel-mounted gauge, a transmitting bulb, and the connecting cables. Different types of gauges are used with different types of transmitters but the principle of operation is the same. A small battery current is passed through the internal circuits of the gauge and through the transmitter bulb to earth. The bulb contains a resistance which is altered in value as its temperature rises. The changes of resistance are sensed by the gauge, which reacts and moves its needle over the dial.

As there are so many systems, it is important that the manufacturer's instructions for testing and fault location should be consulted and followed. It is easy to burn out the instruments by passing the battery current through the wrong terminal.

System maintenance
Air cooled
The only regular work needed is the cleaning of the finning and the clearing and repairing of the ducting system. Where fans are used their drive-belt tension may need periodic adjustment.

Water cooled
The following points should be noted:
(a) Whenever possible use only soft water. In hard water districts, the use of an inhibitor such as potassium dichlorate will reduce the tendency of the limestone deposits in the water to combine with rust to form sludge.
(b) Check the water level at weekly intervals.
(c) Examine the rubber hoses and replace them if dry and cracked, or if oil soaked and spongy. Check the tightness of the clips.
(d) Before installing anti-freeze: (i) check all joints and pipes and renew if necessary, (ii) back flush the system, including the heater, and (iii) mix the anti-freeze with some water, pour into the radiator, top up, and warm up the engine. Top up again when the engine is warm. Retain some of the mixture for subsequent topping-up during the winter.
(e) Check the thermostat and the pressure cap for their correct operation and renew if necessary.

COOLING SYSTEM FAULTS

The most common fault in the cooling system is overheating. This may be caused by:
(a) Shortage of water.
(b) Poor or no circulation of the water.
(c) Poor heat transfer from the engine parts to the water.
(d) Poor heat transfer from the water to the air in the radiator.

The table on the next page sets out the causes of, and remedies for, faults in the cooling system.

Fault	Causes	Remedies
1. Shortage of water	(a) Cracked or pin-holed hoses	Replace by new hoses
	(b) Damaged gaskets	Replace by new gaskets
	(c) Corroded core plugs	Replace by new core plugs
	(d) Slack hose clips	Tighten or replace
	(e) Interior heater damaged	Remove, repair or replace by new heater and pipes
	(f) Radiator cap not seating or holding the correct pressure	Clean seatings or replace with new cap
	(g) Leaking water-pump seals	Adjust, replace, or fit new pump
	(h) Faulty cylinder-head gasket, warped cylinder head, cracked head or wall	Fit new gasket, reface cylinder head and block, specialist repair of block, or fit new sleeve
	(i) Partly blocked radiator core, or head gasket leaking pressure into system, causing water to pass out via overflow	Back flush radiator or fit new unit. Fit new head gasket, check head for flatness and corrosion
2. Circulation poor or nil	(a) Slack fan belt	Tighten to allow up to one inch of play at belt centre. Check for belt bottoming in pulleys
	(b) Thermostat valve out of action, partly closed all the time	Fit new thermostat of correct pressures for system
	(c) Radiator core partly blocked	Back flush radiator or replace by new or serviced unit
	(d) Pump impeller badly corroded	Replace by new pump or impeller
	(e) Pump drive shaft fractured	Replace by new or serviced unit
3. Poor heat transfer to water	(a) Excessive carbon deposits in combustion chambers – heat insulating	Clean out by hand or by using chemical cleaners. In latter case, note danger to zinc and aluminium alloys – very thorough flushing afterwards. Use corrosion inhibitor
	(b) Hard-baked sludge in engine water jackets – heat insulating	
4. Poor heat transfer to the air	(a) Blocked air passages in radiator core	Blow out carefully with air line. Check for obstructions to air flow – muffs, blinds, too many club badges.
	(b) Dirt and sludge in core water tubes – heat insulating. As for fault three	

INTERIOR HEATERS

These are small radiators used to heat the inside of cars and the cabs of commercial vehicles. The element or core may be rectangular or cylindrical in shape and its construction is similar to that of the main radiator. Hot water is supplied directly from a suitable point on the cylinder head of the engine and, after passing through the element, is returned to the cooling system at a point near the intake of the impeller pump. The flow of hot water is controlled either by a tap on the cylinder head or by a valve attached to the jacket of the element. This jacket is a steel or aluminium pressing which encloses the element and directs heated air to the desired areas inside the car. Ducts or pipes of reinforced paper are also fitted to direct heated air over the windscreen. A system of valves enables the driver to control both the areas heated and degree of heating.

Heaters may be classified as recirculatory or fresh-air types. Recirculatory types are usually fitted as extras and are mounted inside the car. They consist of a hot-water heating element and a small electrically-driven fan which can be operated at different speeds by using a variable resistance. The fan causes the air trapped inside the car to circulate through the heater in a continuous stream, i.e. the same air is recirculated.

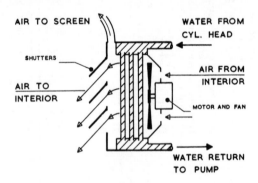

Fig. 7.12 Interior heater: recirculatory type

The objection to this type is that the air quickly becomes stale and tainted, particularly if the occupants are smoking. On a long journey

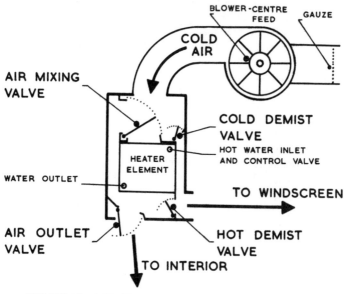

BLOWER-CENTRE FEED

GAUZE

COLD AIR

AIR MIXING VALVE

COLD DEMIST VALVE

HOT WATER INLET AND CONTROL VALVE

HEATER ELEMENT

WATER OUTLET

TO WINDSCREEN

AIR OUTLET VALVE

HOT DEMIST VALVE

TO INTERIOR

GENERAL HEATING

SCREEN CONTROL IN MIDWAY POSITION
CAR CONTROL IN MIDWAY POSITION

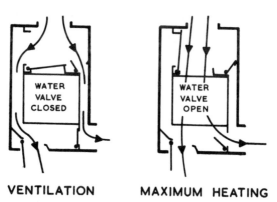

WATER VALVE CLOSED

WATER VALVE OPEN

VENTILATION

SCREEN AT DEFROST
CAR AT COLD

MAXIMUM HEATING

SCREEN AT DE ICE
CAR AT HOT

Fig. 7.13 Interior heater: fresh-air type

this stale air could be a source of danger by making the driver less alert. Dust and other dirt is also drawn into the finning of the element, which is then made less effective as a heater.

The fresh-air types are usually standard fittings, the main units being a heater element and a fairly large electrically-driven fan or blower. The heater element is jacketed, and is mounted in the engine compartment in such a way that it can discharge air into the forward floor areas. The blower may be mounted near the radiator at the front of the vehicle, or near the heater element, and is connected to the element by a large-diameter reinforced paper pipe. When the blower is switched on fresh air is drawn from the intake at the side of the radiator, or the top of the bonnet, and is forced through the jacket of the element. Here it is controlled by flap valves which direct the heated air as required, the water-control valve being inter-connected with the controls of the air valve. In some installations an extra valve is fitted which allows unheated air to pass directly into the car.

In open-road driving the movement of the vehicle is usually sufficient to force air through the jacket of the element into the car, but at standstill and at low road speeds the blower is needed. It should be noted that the use of the blower in heavy traffic conditions may result in the exhaust fumes of other vehicles being drawn into the car. More elaborate installations are fitted in larger and more expensive cars, and these also provide heated air for the comfort of the rear passengers. They may also provide hot air to the rear window.

8 Transmission

Strap drive
In the older types of clutch the drive from the clutch body, or cover, to the pressure plate is obtained via rectangular lugs on the pressure plate, the lugs protruding through close-fitting slots in the cover.

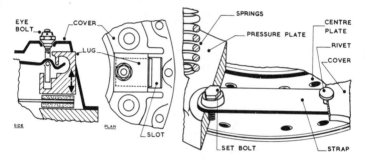

Fig. 8.1. Slot-drive pressure plate   Fig. 8.2 Strap-drive pressure plate

This arrangement results in friction between lugs and cover, and eventually causes wear, squeaks, rattles and loss of balance as the pressure plate moves in relation to the flywheel and the cover.

These disadvantages are eliminated by the use of flexible steel straps. These are arranged in pairs, tangentially between the cover and the pressure plate, in such a way that the pressure plate is always kept concentric with the case and the flywheel but is free to move to release the centre plate. In the Borg & Beck clutches of this type the straps are riveted to the cover and bolted to the pressure plate.

Diaphragm spring clutch
Advantages over normal clutch
(1) Fewer components.

(2) More compact – can allow a larger diameter of centre plate for the same overall cover diameter.

(3) Less effort required for releasing and holding disengaged.

(4) Simpler mechanism for withdrawal of pressure plate.

(5) Automatic compensation for lining wear.

(6) Spring thrust remains constant at all speeds.

Borg and Beck type

Construction

In these clutches a steel diaphragm spring is used to force the pressure plate towards the flywheel. This spring is a saucer shaped disc,

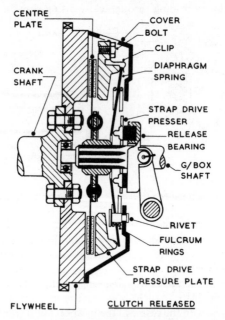

Fig. 8.3 Diaphragm clutch

of hardened and tempered steel, which has radially arranged slots cut from the hollow centre towards the outer edge. Shouldered rivets, which pass through elongated holes at the outer ends of the slots, secure the diaphragm to the clutch cover. These rivets also hold in position the fulcrum rings on which the diaphragm pivots. These rings are of circular cross-section and one ring is fitted at each side of the diaphragm. The outer edge of the diaphragm is located on the pressure plate by a series of bolted clips, and the pressure plate is driven by straps. The presser plate of the thrust release bearing abuts the centre of the diaphragm spring and is secured to the cover by three tangentially-arranged flexible steel straps. The centre plate is of the flexible, or spring-drive, type.

Operation
When the clutch assembly is bolted to the flywheel, the diaphragm spring is flattened and exerts a powerful thrust on the pressure plate – so trapping the centre plate firmly between it and the flywheel. When the clutch is disengaged, the centre of the diaphragm is forced inwards. The diaphragm pivots between the fulcrum rings and its outer edge (acting through the clips), withdraws the pressure plate, and releases the centre plate.

A characteristic of the diaphragm spring is that it exerts its maximum thrust when it is flattened. This results in less effort being required to release the clutch, and also in less effort being needed to hold it out than to initially disengage it. By the correct positioning of the fulcrums, these clutches, unlike the conventional types, can be made to maintain the spring thrust at a constant value – in spite of the effects of lining wear and high speeds of rotation. Ball bearing, or carbon block, types of release thrust bearing may be fitted.

Centre plates
Clutch units must have the following features:
(a) A smooth and gradual 'take-up' of the crankshaft torque – no slip, snatch or judder.
(b) A clean-cut interruption or break in the transmission of torque – no drag or spin.
(c) The ability to absorb small torque irregularities which would otherwise result in transmission noise and extra stress and wear.
(d) The ability to dissipate heat.

To a large extent these important features are realized by using carefully designed and constructed centre plates. These consist essentially of a light-weight, hardened and tempered, flexible steel disc which has a relatively heavy steel hub at its centre. The hub is splined and is carried upon the splined gearbox input, or spigot shaft. An annulus-shaped friction lining of asbestos-based material is riveted to each side of the disc. Some linings are now chemically bonded to the disc. Centre plates may be rigid or flexible and there are different forms of each type.

Rigid types
In these there is no relative movement between the linings and the disc, and the hub. The disc is annulus-shaped and is riveted to the hub. The linings are riveted to dished steel segments which are themselves riveted around the circumference of the disc. In another form the disc itself is slotted radially and the resulting segments are 'set' alternately – rather like the teeth of a saw. This alternate off-setting of the segments is called 'crimping', and the linings at each side are riveted to alternate segments. The combination of these two arrangements results in the linings moving apart when the clutch is disengaged, i.e. they can flex on the flywheel. The effects of crimping are to:
(a) Make the centre plate move away from the flywheel when the clutch is disengaged – reducing drag.

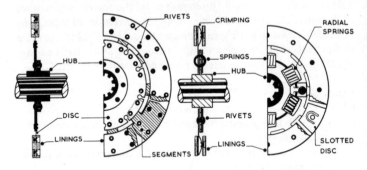

Fig. 8.4 Rigid centre plate   Fig. 8.5 Flexible centre plate

(b) Provide a more gradual and smoother engagement – the linings being forced together over a greater distance of pedal travel – no snatch or judder.
(c) Allow air to pass between the linings to carry away heat while the clutch is disengaged – coefficient of friction maintained.

Rigid types are usually to be found in multi-plate clutches, in heavy commercial vehicles, and in racing and trials cars.

Flexible types

In these a certain amount of radical movement is allowed between the linings and the disc, and the hub. The disc and its lining-carrying segments are similar to those of the rigid types, but the only connection between the disc and its hub is made through a set of radially disposed springs. These are fitted into slots formed in the hub, and in the disc and its support, and the ends of the springs press very hard against the ends of the slots. The disc and the hub are riveted together but the rivet holes through the hub are elongated to permit the required radial movement. The extent of the movement is controlled by the springs. These are compressed as the drive is first taken up (the disc moving while the hub is held back) and then they extend to their normal length as the hub follows the disc. The action of the springs is therefore to absorb or cushion the inevitable shock of connecting shafts which are running at different speeds. They also absorb small torque irregularities during normal running.

In another form of flexible centre plate the hub and the disc are both chemically bonded to a disc made from a special form of rubber. This rubber, as it is distorted at take-up, has the same cushioning effect as the radial springs. In some heavy vehicle clutches the cushioning effect is obtained by the use of a Layrub type of joint to connect the hub to the disc.

Lining materials

The material most commonly used for clutch linings has an asbestos base. This is a fibrous mineral which can be woven or powdered. After being mixed with resins and other binding materials, and possibly being reinforced by zinc or brass wire, it is compressed into moulds of the required shape, and is then baked.

As a lining material the finished product has a coefficient of friction, when used dry with steel, of about 0.3 and this does not reduce very much as its temperature is increased in operation. It is a fairly hard-wearing material which can resist high temperatures and pressures, and to some extent it is oil resistant. When the linings have been riveted to the disc they should be ground to make certain that their faces are at right angles to the axis of the plate. In some modern plates the linings may be chemically bonded to the disc.

Clutch brakes

When centre plates have to be of relatively large diameter and weight they tend to keep rotating too long after the clutch is released, i.e. they suffer badly from 'spin'. As this makes gear changing very difficult, many of the larger clutches incorporate some form of clutch brake. This is brought into operation during the final movements of the release mechanism, a pad or disc lined with friction material being forced into contact with a disc attached either to the centre plate hub or to the gearbox input shaft.

Multiplate clutches

These may be wet or dry types and, because of their increased number of friction faces in contact, they can operate efficiently with individually weaker springs. This makes them smoother and easier to operate than the equivalent single-plate type.

Multiplate clutches may be used:

(a) Where space is very limited, e.g. in automatic transmissions and in motor cycles. In the latter a multi-plate clutch of *small diameter* transmits approximately the *same torque* as a single-plate clutch of more than twice its diameter.

(b) Where very large torques have to be transmitted, e.g. in heavy commercial vehicles, racing cars, and special-purpose military and agricultural vehicles. In these the increased number of plates provides the increased torque-transmitting ability of the clutch.

Smaller types

Probably the most common use of the multiplate clutch in vehicles is in pre-selector gearboxes, and in automatic transmissions. In these units the clutches are similar to those used in some motor cycles, i.e. wet metal-plate types. The plates are annulus-shaped and the driving and driven plates are arranged alternately. The driving plates are themselves driven through their external lugs which project through slots in a cover bolted to the flywheel or other driving member. The driven plates in turn drive the gearbox shaft or other driven member through their internal lugs which fit into splines. One set of plates may be of steel and the other of phosphor bronze, or sintered bronze which is porous and so retains oil. As the plates operate in oil at all times their life is long and

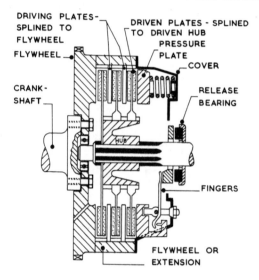

Fig. 8.6 Multi-plate clutch

a smooth take-up is obtained. The plates are all forced towards the driving member by radially arranged springs, and a simple release mechanism is provided.

Commercial vehicle types

These are usually dry, two-plate types. Their construction is similar to the normal clutch but the flywheel is deeply recessed. Two separate, rigid type, centre plates are carried by the gearbox input shaft, and the intermediate and the pressure plate are peg driven by the flywheel. About twenty thrust springs are fitted, and the release fingers are mounted on needle roller bearings. A clutch brake is incorporated with a heavy-duty ball bearing release mechanism.

Centrifugal clutches

Semi-centrifugal type

These are really improved versions of the normal single-plate type, and are pedal operated in the normal way. They have the usual form of construction, but the important difference lies in the design and action of the release levers or fingers. Three of these are fitted, and each is suspended and pivoted on a boss bolted to the clutch cover, the pivots consisting of two rollers inside a hardened bush. Outward of these pivots the fingers are connected to lugs on the pressure plate, needle roller bearings being used. The outer ends of the fingers are formed into small weights which project through the cover.

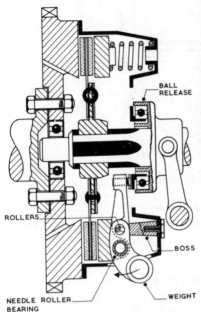

ROLLERS

NEEDLE ROLLER
BEARING

Fig. 8.7 Semi-centrifugal clutch

When the clutch is rotating, centrifugal force, acting through the finger weights, causes the fingers to turn about the boss pivots – forcing the pressure plate towards the flywheel and thus assisting the action of the thrust springs. When the clutch pedal is depressed the fingers again turn about the boss pivots and draw the pressure plate away from the centre plate and the flywheel. The assistance obtained from the centrifugal forces reduces slip at high speeds and, by making possible the use of lighter thrust springs, makes the clutch easier to operate.

Fully centrifugal type

These engage and release automatically according to the speed of the engine. Most may be regarded as single-plate types in which the clutch assembly is held away from the flywheel, and against a stop ring, by a second set of radially disposed outer springs. Three weighted levers turn on cover-mounted pivots to force the assembly towards the flywheel under centrifugal force. Flexible-type centre plates are usually fitted.

At idling speeds, the centrifugal forces acting upon the lever weights are insufficient to overcome the force due to the set of outer springs. The pressure plate assembly does not therefore contact the centre plate and no crankshaft torque is transmitted.

As the engine speed is increased, the centrifugal forces also increase – but under the square law (twice the speed = four times the force) – and the levers are turned on their pivots. This action forces the pressure-plate assembly to move inwards, compressing the outer springs and forcing the centre plate to transmit torque. The higher the engine speed the greater the torque transmitted. The movement of the levers is limited by stops to avoid excessive slip at slow speeds, and excessive pressures on the linings at very high speeds.

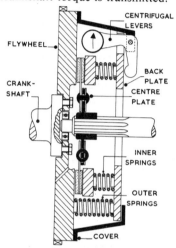

Fig. 8.8 Centrifugal clutch

In the Borg & Beck centrifugal clutch, weighted levers are pivoted on a reactor plate fitted inside the cover. As the centrifugal forces increase the levers move outwards and away from their low-speed stops. This forces small struts to move inwards and engage the pressure plate with the centre plate, so starting the transmission of torque. As the speed increases so slip is reduced until, when the levers touch their high speed stops, the maximum possible torque is transmitted.

The engagement of this type is particularly smooth, and the linings have a longer service life than a similar but manually operated type.

Release mechanisms
Mechanical
In the mechanical release systems the pedal is pivoted on a short

shaft secured to the chassis. A lever-operated cross shaft is fitted through the clutch bell housing, at 90° to the gearbox input shaft and below it, and the shaft carries a fork connected to a carbon or ball-release thrust bearing. The connection between the lever on the end of the cross shaft and the lower end of the pedal may be made by the use of rods, chain, or Bowden cable. A pedal return spring is fitted at some suitable point.

As the friction linings wear, the pressure plate moves closer to the flywheel. The release fingers follow this movement and as they pivot their release pad ends move out towards the gearbox. This reduces the clearance of the release bearing and causes the clutch to slip. The clearance and the free play of the pedal are restored by adjusting the length of the linkage between the pedal and the cross-shaft lever. An adjusting nut and a lock nut are usually fitted, and it is a trial-and-error process.

Hydraulic

Mechanical systems of clutch operation were used for many years, and are still used in the heavier vehicles. While they were adequate for more or less rigidly mounted engine and clutch assemblies they are unsuitable for modern and smaller engine installations. In these the engines are arranged much lower in the chassis, and they are carried in very flexible mountings which allow considerable movement between the clutch and the pedal. Judder, caused by engine movement, has been eliminated by the use of hydraulic systems of clutch operation.

The hydraulic systems consist of a master cylinder, a relay or slave cylinder, and a strong connecting pipe. The system must be full of fluid and free of air at all times. The force exerted at the pedal is converted, by the master cylinder, into pressure on the fluid. In the slave cylinder the pressure is at once converted back into a force which moves the cross shaft to disengage the clutch. When the clutch is released the thrust springs act to return the slave piston, which in turn forces the fluid back to the master cylinder. A standing fluid pressure is not maintained and there is no check valve in the master cylinder.

Where both the brakes and the clutch are hydraulically operated the pedals are usually of the suspended type. Two separate master cylinders, or one twin-bore master cylinder, may be fitted. The

169

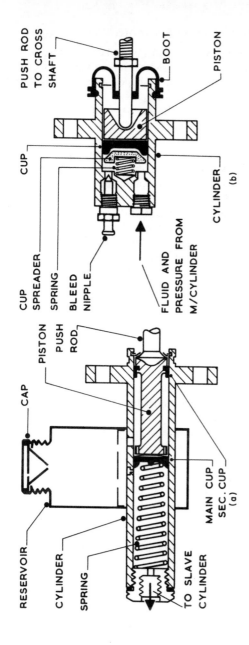

Fig. 8.9 Hydraulic system: (a) clutch master cylinder; (b) clutch slave cylinder

slave cylinder is clamped or bolted to the bell housing, with its push rod connected to the cross-shaft lever. In many vehicles the cross shaft is now replaced by a Y-shaped steel pressing carried on a ball pivot inside the bell housing.

NOTE. The feel of the pedal in these systems gives no reliable indication of the existence or otherwise of a clearance at the release bearing.

In the Lockheed system, the push rod of the master cylinder must be adjusted to provide 4 mm clearance between the end of the rod and the piston. This ensures an adequate clearance for the release bearing. Where lining wear is automatically compensated, e.g. in units with a diaphragm spring, no other adjustment is provided. Where the older type of clutch is used, in which lining wear results in the loss of the release bearing clearance, an adjustment is provided on the slave push rod. This must be set to give a clearance of 1·5 mm between the end of the push rod and the cross or Y shaft. This latter adjustment will need checking at intervals during the life of the clutch.

Bleeding. This operation should only be necessary when the system has been opened or damaged.
(1) Fill the reservoir, and keep checking the level and topping up at intervals.
(2) Attach the bleed pipe to the bleed screw on the slave cylinder and submerge the free end under the surface of a small quantity of fluid in a glass jar.
(3) Slacken off the bleed screw and press the pedal down *slowly*. Tighten the bleed screw *before* the pedal reaches the end of its travel.
(4) Allow the pedal to return unaided.
(5) Repeat the sequence until no bubbles of air can be seen emerging from the tube. Tighten the bleed screw and remove the pipe.

Table 8.1 sets out the most common clutch faults – with causes and remedies.

Table 8.1 Fault diagnosis

Fault	Cause	Remedies
Slip Clutch does not transmit the available engine torque	1. Inadequate free play at pedal	Adjust to correct free movement
	2. Pedal not returning fully	Free and lubricate linkages. Check for floor-board fouling pedal
	3. Oil or grease on linings	Locate source of oil and rectify (rear main) Clean metal faces and fit new centre plate
	4. Excessively worn linings	Fit new centre plate
	5. Weak thrust springs	Fit replacement clutch assembly, or fit new springs
	6. Scored faces on flywheel and pressure plate	Regrind or replace with new flywheel and assembly
Drag or spin Centre plate is not fully free of torque	1. Excessive free play at pedal	Adjust to correct free movement
	2. Baked, sticky oil or grease on linings	As 3 for slip
	3. Crimping of centre plate damaged	Fit new centre plate
	4. Centre plate not parallel to flywheel	Fit new centre plate. Check alignment of spigot shaft
	5. Hub splines excessively worn	Fit new centre plate and spigot shaft
	6. Thrust bearing excessively worn	Fit new release bearing
	7. Fingers or levers damaged or incorrectly set	Replace fingers or assembly, or reset fingers
	8. Spigot bearing or bush binding on shaft	Clean and lubricate or replace with new bearing
	9. Rusted or dirty splines on hub and shaft	Clean and lightly oil
	10. Spigot shaft bent	Fit new shaft
	11. Distorted or cracked flywheel or pressure plate	Regrind or replace with new units
	12. Clutch brake not operating properly	Adjust to correct settings or reline pad

(See over page)

Fault	Cause	Remedies
Judder and snatch Fierce take up of drive	1. Slack engine-to-chassis tie bar	Adjust to correct tension
	2. Engine rubber mountings loose or perished	Tighten or replace with new mountings
	3. Baked, dry oil or grease on linings	Locate source and rectify. Clean metal plates, fit new centre plate
	4. Excessively worn or loose linings	Fit new centre plate
	5. Crimping of centre plate damaged	Fit new centre plate
	6. Centre plate springs slack in slots	Fit new centre plate
	7. Distorted centre or pressure plate	Fit new plate or clutch assembly
	8. Release mechanism sticking	Release and lubricate
	9. Bent spigot shaft	Fit new shaft
Rattle	1. Pedal return spring missing or broken	Fit new spring
	2. Excessively worn release mechanism	Replace worn parts
	3. Carbon release bearing loose in holder	Fit new thrust carbon pad
	4. Finger springs weak or broken	Fit new finger springs (anti-rattle springs)
	5. Centre plate springs loose or rivets slack	Fit new centre plate
	6. Gearbox shaft and bearing excessively worn	Fit new shaft and bearing
Knock	1. Excessively worn spigot bearing	Fit new bearing. Check shaft for excessive wear
	2. Excessively worn centre plate hub splines	Fit new centre plate, check shaft splines for excessive wear
Whine or whistle	1. Excessively worn release ball bearing	Fit new bearing
	2. Dry release ball bearing	Lubricate or fit prepacked bearing
Pedal throw	1. Fingers broken	Fit new fingers and adjust or replace clutch assembly
	2. Fingers unevenly adjusted	Adjust to correct settings. Check thrust

THE GEARBOX

Selector mechanism

The mechanism by which a particular gear train is selected, or brought into operation, consists essentially of a fork which can be moved parallel to the longitudinal axis of the gearbox in either a forward or backward direction. Provision must be made for automatically locking the selector fork in its required position, and also for preventing the movement of more than one selector fork at any one time.

Selector forks

The selector fork must be tough and rigid, and hard wearing, and may be made of phosphor or aluminium bronze. The top of the fork is approximately tubular in shape and has a vertical lug in which is machined a rectangular slot. The lower end of the gear lever is engaged with this slot as required. The lower, and forked end, of the selector fork is approximately semicircular and is at 90° to the axis of the tubular portion. Some forked parts are flat and engage in grooves machined in extensions of the gears or in synchromesh hubs. In others the forks may be of an inverted U cross-section, and this type fits over the gears or over raised faces on the hubs.

A three-speed and reverse gearbox has two selector shafts and forks, while a four-speed and reverse gearbox has three. Each fork is carried upon a selector shaft of case-hardened steel, the shaft passing through the tubular top of the fork and being supported in the top or end walls of the box. In some gearboxes the forks are locked to the shafts and both are moved during selection; in others the forks slide upon the shafts. In the latter type the shafts are prevented from rotating by anchor plates.

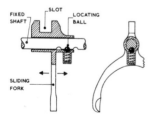

Fig. 8.10 Selector fork

Selector locks

The selector forks are locked into position by spring-loaded steel balls, or by ball-ended plungers, which engage with semicircular grooves machined in the selector shafts. In a three-speed and reverse gearbox each shaft has three grooves – one for each gear train and one for neutral. In a four-speed and reverse gearbox the two selector shafts for the forward speeds each have three grooves while the reverse selector shaft has only two. Where the forks move on the shafts the spring-loaded balls or plungers are fitted inside the top of the fork and the grooves are positioned to suit this arrangement. Where the forks are locked to the shafts, by a small, spigoted, set bolt, the balls or plungers are fitted inside the gearbox top or in the end walls.

Lever arrangements

Box top. The most common arrangement of the gear-change lever is that in which the lever is passed through a small tower on the top of the gearbox, the lever pivoting on a hemispherical seating inside the tower. A peg in the side of the tower is engaged with a vertical slot in the lever sphere and so prevents the axial rotation of the lever. The lower end of the lever is fitted into the rectangular slots of the selector fork tubular portions, and is so shaped that it can move any fork without locking itself in the slots.

Steering column. Some cars are fitted with bench-type front seats and when these are fitted the gear-change lever may be mounted

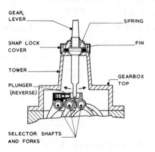

Fig. 8.11 Box-top arrangement
(tower type)

upon the steering column. In this arrangement, for a three-speed gearbox, the selector shafts are fitted at the side of the box and are moved by individual levers on short shafts. The levers are connected by rods to relay levers pivoting upon the chassis. These levers are in turn connected by adjustable rods to selector levers bolted to the lower end of the steering column. The gear-change lever is mounted at the upper end of the column, under the steering wheel, and can be moved up and down parallel with the wheel, and also with the column. The inner end of this lever connects with either one of the selector levers at the foot of the column through one of two sets of dogs. Normally the change lever is spring-loaded to select top or second gear in one movement, and has to be lifted or depressed to obtain first or reverse gear. When a four-speed box is used, the linkage is made more complicated by the need to provide a third lever or cable system for reverse selection.

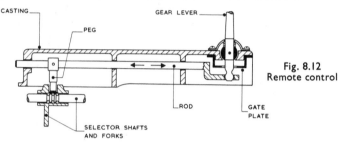

Fig. 8.12
Remote control

Remote control. A remote-control mechanism for gear-changing is fitted in vehicles where the gearbox is inconveniently distant from the driving position. These may be sports cars, cars with rear power units, or passenger transport vehicles. In one arrangement used in cars the control consists of a long aluminium-alloy casting which is bolted to the top of the gearbox. The free end supports and locates a short and straight gear lever, the lower end of the lever passing through a gate plate and being connected to a long and stiff rod. The forward end of this rod is fitted with the specially shaped peg which engages with the slots in the tops of the selector forks. The movement of the gear lever is thus followed by the peg to select the required gear train.

Interlock mechanisms

It is important that it be impossible to select more than one gear train at one time! This is ensured by the use of automatic selector locks. The accidental selection of reverse gear may also be made less likely by giving it a more unusual or more complicated lever movement, e.g. lifting, forcing hard to one side, or having first to depress a thumb button. The interlocks are arranged inside the gearbox, and in one form the lock consists of a flat, rectangular plate of steel slotted to fit over the lugs of the selector fork without restricting their movement. Pivoting on top of this plate is a second plate shaped approximately like a pair of calipers, the jaw ends resting in the slots in the selector fork. As the gap between the jaws is only slightly wider than the fork lugs, and than the end of the gear lever, only the selected fork can move between them. In this type, the forks move on the shafts.

Where the shafts move with the forks a different form of interlock is necessary. In the three-speed gearbox the two shafts are each grooved at the same end. The grooves face each other and, in the neutral position, each is aligned with the ends of a hole drilled through the box top. In this hole is fitted a free sliding ball or ball-ended plunger, the length of which is such that when one selector shaft is moved it forces the plunger into the groove of the other shaft – so preventing its movement. A similar arrangement is used in the four-speed gearbox but the central selector shaft has a groove at each side. The plunger passes through this shaft at the groove position, and each end of the plunger is in contact with a steel ball. When one shaft is moved the other two are automatically locked by the steel balls.

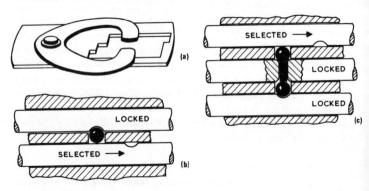

Fig. 8.13 Interlock mechanisms: (a) plate interlock; (b) three-speed interlock; (c) four-speed interlock

Synchromesh gearbox

These are similar to the equivalent constant-mesh, dog-clutch types in general arrangement but have synchronizing cones operating in conjunction with the dogs. Their main features are:

(1) The output (mainshaft) gears are free to rotate on bushes on the output shaft and are located by internally splined thrust washers. Single or double helical gears are used and they are in constant mesh with the layshaft gears.

(2) When selected, the output gears are locked to their shaft by the dog clutch of their synchronizing hub – after their speeds have been equalized, or synchronized, by their cones.

Note that when changing gear the speed of the *output gears*, and of the layshaft, has to be *synchronized with* that of *the output shaft* – which is being driven by the driving road wheels.

Synchronizing hubs: constant load type

These consist of an inner and outer hub, or gear coupling. The inner hub is splined to the gearbox output shaft and is free to

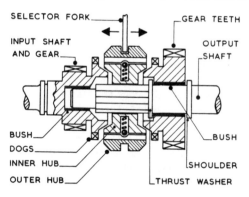

Fig. 8.14 Constant-load synchromesh unit

move slightly along it. This hub has an internal conical face, lined with phosphor bronze, at each side facing external conical faces on each gear. Above and inward of the gear faces is a series of splines which act as one half of a dog clutch. The outer hub is splined to the inner hub and is located centrally upon it by a set of spring-loaded steel balls. The splines are identical in shape and pitch to those on the gears.

When the clutch is disengaged, and the gear lever and the selector fork are moved to engage a fresh gear train, the first part of the movement forces both hubs to move slightly along the output shaft. (The hubs are held together laterally by their radial balls and springs.) This movement brings the conical face of the inner hub into contact with the face of the gear – and brings the selected gear and the layshaft up to the speed of the output shaft, i.e. the gear is synchronized with the shaft.

Continued gear-lever movement then overcomes the holding action of the radial balls and springs, and the outer hub is moved laterally to engage its splines with those of the gear. In this way the gear is locked to its shaft and, as the clutch is engaged, engine torque is transmitted to the output shaft through the layshaft, the output gear, the outer hub, and the inner hub.

Three-speed type
In the modern types of three-speed gearbox all three forward speeds are synchromesh, the first (low) gear being obtained by using a special hub. This has only one conical face and the outer hub is also the reverse output gear – moving in one direction to lock the first gear to its shaft and in the opposite direction to slide into mesh with the reverse idler gear.

The disadvantage of the constant load hub is the time taken for the cones to synchronize. This depends upon the frictional forces between the cones and will vary with the mechanical condition of the hubs, and with the viscosity of the oil. Even if these are as intended by the designer a careless or 'clever' driver can still cause damage by rushing the change. This driving fault is known as 'beating the cones' and it results in noise, erratic selection, and the later failure of the synchromesh unit. The later types of unit are so constructed that the dogs cannot be engaged, or even moved, until the gear and the shaft are fully synchronized. These are known as baulking ring or inertia lock types.

Baulk ring type. A number of different forms of baulking ring unit are in service. In one form the inner hub is splined both to the output shaft and to the outer hub, which may be a sliding mesh gear in some gearboxes. The outer splined surface of the inner hub has

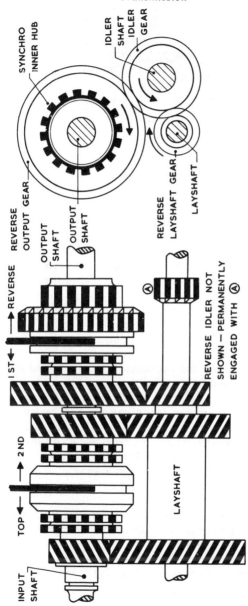

SYNCHRO INNER HUB

IDLER SHAFT

IDLER GEAR

REVERSE OUTPUT GEAR

OUTPUT GEAR

OUTPUT SHAFT

OUTPUT SHAFT

REVERSE LAYSHAFT GEAR

LAYSHAFT

Fig. 8.16 Reverse gear, three-speed

REVERSE

1 ST

2 ND

TOP

INPUT SHAFT

REVERSE IDLER NOT SHOWN — PERMANENTLY ENGAGED WITH Ⓐ

Ⓐ

Ⓐ

LAYSHAFT

Fig. 8.15 Three-speed synchromesh gearbox

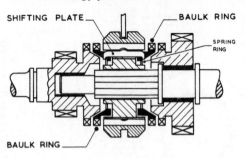

Fig. 8.17 Baulk ring synchromesh unit

three lateral grooves in each of which is fitted a rectangular shifting plate. The plates are located by spring-loaded steel balls fitting into a shallow groove in the outer hub or by spring rings. The friction, or baulking, conical rings are separate units of phosphor bronze which fit loosely over the conical faces of the gears. The rings carry dogs identical to those on the gear and in the outer hub. The cones are slotted to coincide with the shifting plates, the slots being the width of the plates plus the pitch of the dogs. In their neutral or engaged position a clearance equal to half the pitch of the dogs exists at each side of the plates. All the splines are chamfered.

When the gear lever and the selector fork are moved the first part of the movement forces the outer hub and the shifting plates towards the gear. The shifting plates force the baulking ring into light contact with the conical face of the gear and, because of the different speeds of rotation, the ring is moved round until it takes up the clearance between the shifting plates and their slots, i.e. it is moved half the pitch of the dogs relative to the outer hub. At this point the baulking ring dogs are out of alignment with the other dogs and so are preventing (baulking) any further movement of the outer hub.

If a larger force is now applied to the gear lever the dogs of the outer hub, acting through the chamfered ends of the dogs, will apply a greater force to the baulking ring – and so will speed up the synchronization action. As the two speeds equalize the shifting plates centralize in the ring slots and the ring dogs align themselves with the other dogs. This allows the outer hub to pass over the dogs of the baulking ring to engage fully with the dogs of the gear. Selection is now completed.

The characteristics of the baulking-ring type of synchromesh unit are that (1) the force or load on the cones increases automatically as the speed of the gear change is increased, and (2) the dogs cannot be engaged unless the speed of the gear and of the output shaft are the same.

Four-speed type

In general layout the four-speed, fully synchromesh gearbox is similar to that of the constant-mesh, dog-clutch type which it has largely replaced. Single or double helical gears are employed, together with two synchromesh units of either constant-load or baulking-ring type. The first unit is fitted between the input gear and the third speed output gear while the second unit is fitted between the second and the first output gears. The sliding outer hub of this second synchronizer carries an integral spur-toothed gear which, in the neutral position, is aligned with a spur gear on the layshaft. When reverse is selected the single-spur idler gear is moved into mesh with the layshaft and the outer gear to reverse the direction of the output torque.

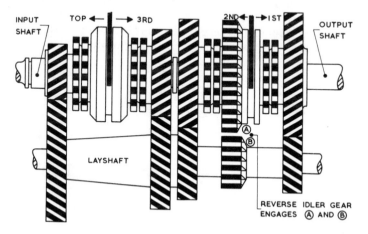

Fig. 8.18 Four-speed synchromesh gearbox

Tailshaft extension

In many modern cars the rear of the gearbox, and the output or tail shaft are considerably extended. This permits the use of a shorter and more rigid propeller shaft. It also allows the fitting of an extra bush or bearing to provide extra support to the output shaft. The effect of this is to reduce stress and wear generally, but in particular it reduces wear at the spigot bearing inside the input shaft, i.e. the two shafts are maintained in more accurate alignment. In many arrangements the forward end of the propeller shaft is connected to a sliding yoke which is supported by the tailshaft bush. A spring-loaded leather or plastic oil seal is fitted outward of the bush or bearing.

Bearings

The devices used to support and locate the shafts and the gears in vehicle gearboxes include ball bearings; parallel, taper, and needle roller bearings; bushes; and thrust washers and circlips. Spring-loaded steel balls and plungers are used to ensure the temporary location of various parts.

The forward end of the input (spigot) shaft is supported by either a bush or a ball bearing fitted into the centre of the flywheel. The bush may be of the porous and oil-retaining sintered bronze type. The bearing may be pre-packed with lubricant and sealed. Self-aligning ball bearings are also used at this point. The inner end of the input shaft is supported in, and located by, a ball bearing. This is secured to the shaft by either a shoulder and a nut and

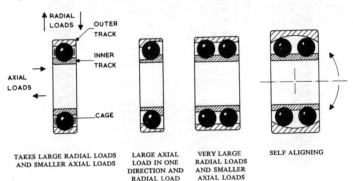

TAKES LARGE RADIAL LOADS AND SMALLER AXIAL LOADS

LARGE AXIAL LOAD IN ONE DIRECTION AND RADIAL LOAD

VERY LARGE RADIAL LOADS AND SMALLER AXIAL LOADS

SELF ALIGNING

Fig. 8.19 Ball bearings

lock plate, or by means of a circlip, such that the shaft cannot move laterally in the inner track of the bearing. An oil thrower ring, or a chip shield, is fitted between the bearing and the gear. The outer track of the bearing is prevented from moving laterally in the gearbox wall by a circlip. This is fitted into a recess in the outer track and in another recess in the end wall, and is retained by the front cover of the bearing. An oil return thread or a spring-loaded oil seal is incorporated in this cover to prevent oil passing into the clutch assembly.

The inner end of the output shaft is spigoted and is supported inside the inner end of the input shaft by either a sintered bronze bush or a needle roller bearing. The outer end of the shaft is supported in a ball bearing fitted into the rear wall of the gearbox. The inner track of this bearing is located by a shoulder at one side and the drive plate of the propeller shaft at the other. The outer track is located in the rear end wall of the gearbox by either a circlip and a rear cover plate, or by a shoulder in the wall and a cover plate. A spring-loaded oil seal is fitted to prevent oil escaping. Where a tailshaft extension is fitted an extra bush or bearing, which increases the rigidity of the output shaft, is used at the rearmost end. An oil seal will also be fitted here.

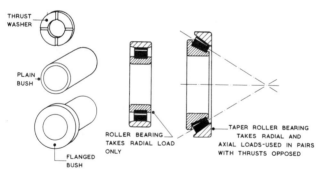

Fig. 8.20 Roller bearings and bushes

The output gears rotate upon bronze bushes which are splined or keyed to the shaft. The reverse idler may rotate on bronze bushes. The gears are located by bronze thrust washers which are themselves located by circlips or shoulders.

The layshaft may rotate upon bronze bushes or needle roller bearings, and is located by bronze thrust washers fitted at each end. In the larger and heavier gearboxes the layshaft is usually supported by ball bearings, circlips, and cover plates. In the gearboxes of very heavy vehicles, a parallel roller bearing may be used at each end to take the radial load, together with a special ball-thrust bearing at the rear end to take the axial load. All the cover plates must be fitted with gaskets to make them oil-tight.

Flushing

This is done to remove accumulated dirt and metal particles, and to keep clear the small oilways which feed the various bushes. The oil is drained off as completely as possible when hot and is about two-thirds replaced by flushing oil. The engine is then run at a fast idle for five minutes to circulate the flushing oil and loosen the dirt. The dirty oil is then drained off and the gearbox refilled to the correct level with recommended oil.

Table 8.2 Fault diagnosis

Fault	Cause	Remedy
Gear lever hard to move	Clutch not releasing fully	See clutch faults.
	Lever ball joint binding	Clean, oil, replace
	Box top incorrectly fitted	Re-align (dowels)
	Remote control out of alignment. Column control rods and joint is incorrectly set, dry or fouling	Re-align Re-set and oil
	Synchromesh units damaged	Replace with new
Gears difficult to engage	Clutch not releasing fully	See clutch faults
	Selector operating levers or forks seized or bent	Release or re-set
	Synchromesh units damaged	Replace with new
	Shortage of lubricant	Fill to correct level, correct oil
	Lubricant too viscous	Replace with oil of correct viscosity
Gears difficult to release	Selector rods or forks partly seized	Free off or replace
	Synchromesh cones seized	Replace unit
	Clutch not releasing fully	See clutch faults

Fault	Cause	Remedy
Gears slipping out of mesh	Weak or broken selector springs	Replace with new gear units
	Excessively worn selector shafts, balls, plungers	Replace with new gear units
	Excessively worn gear teeth or bushes.	Replace with new gear units
	Excessively worn bearings	Replace with new gear units
	Excessively worn dog clutch teeth	Replace with new gear units
Torque not being transmitted:		
(a) in any gear	Input or output shaft broken	Replace or fit new gearbox
(b) except in top gear	Input and layshaft gears stripped of teeth	Replace or fit new gearbox
(c) in any one gear	Teeth or dogs of that gear stripped	Replace or fit new gearbox
Noise:		
(a) whine	Shortage of lubricant	Fill to correct level, correct oil
	Excessively worn bearings, bushes, gear teeth	Replace or fit new gearbox
	Incorrectly aligned gears	Re-align (thrust washers)
(b) knocking or ticking	Chipped gear tooth or ball or roller	Replace with new
	Metal chips loose in box	Remove, determine origin, repair as necessary
Oil leakage	Excessive quantity of oil	Drain to correct level
	Oil viscosity too low for the gearbox	Drain off, replace with correct oil
	Excessively or damaged oil seals or gaskets	Replace with new
	Excessively worn bearings	Replace with new
Excessive free play (backlash) through box	Excessive wear at:	
	(a) spigot shaft splines and internal bush	Replace with new
	(b) Thrust washers and bearings, teeth and dogs	Replace with new

9   Steering

The steering system of the vehicle must:
(a) Enable the driver to control accurately the path taken by the vehicle at all times.
(b) Be light and easy to operate.
(c) Be self centring.
(d) Be as direct as possible in action.
(e) Not be affected by the action of the suspension and braking systems.

The complete steering system consists of a steering wheel and gearbox, and a system of rods, levers, and ball pin joints which transmit the motion of the drop arm of the steering gearbox to

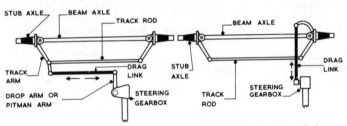

Fig. 9.1 Transverse drag link   Fig. 9.2 Longitudinal drag link

the track arms of the swivelling stub axles. Where a beam axle is used, the drop arm is connected to the track arm of one stub axle by the drag link. The track arm of the opposite stub axle is connected to the first track arm by a track rod. This may be arranged longitudinally or transversely and is adjustable in length. It may be fitted behind or in front of the axle, its function being to keep the front wheels parallel with each other when the vehicle is running straight forward. The drag link may or may not be adjustable, and it is so arranged that its operation is not affected by the movement of the axle and the springs.

The various rods and links are connected by ball pin joints which permit movement in more than one plane. These joints may or may not be adjustable, and are spring loaded to take up wear and free play. They may be pre-packed with lubricant or require lubricating at regular intervals. They must be protected from the entry of dirt and water.

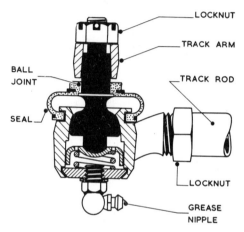

Fig. 9.3 Ball joint

When independent front suspensions (IFS) are used, the steering system has to be modified. A commonly used system employs a three-piece track rod and a transfer or idler box and lever. The drop arm is horizontal and its end is connected to the centre track rod, the opposite end of the track rod being connected to the end of the pivoting idler arm. Short outer track rods are fitted at each side to connect the drop arm and the idler arm to the track arms of their respective stub axles. The length and position of the short track arms are such that the operation of the suspension does not seriously affect the steering. Either the centre track rod, or each of the outer track rods, is adjustable in length.

In an alternative arrangement the track rod is made in two parts,

the drag link operating an L-shaped lever connected at its opposite
end to the inner end of each half track rod. In yet another arrangement the rack of a rack-and-pinion steering gearbox is used as the
centre track rod and a short, adjustable track rod connects the
ends of the rack to the track arm at each side. In a number of IFS

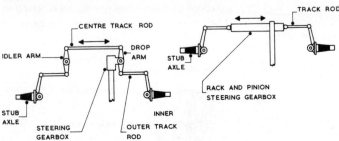

Fig. 9.4 Three-piece track rod   Fig. 9.5 Split track rod

designs the stub axle is bolted to a steel forging which replaces
the kingpin and which is secured to the suspension arms or wish-
bones by ball joints.

Geometry
True rolling motion
In order to provide effective control of the steering of the vehicle,
and to reduce tyre and bearing wear, it is important that the wheels
rotate, under all conditions, with a true rolling motion, i.e. free
from side drag (tyre scrub).

When the vehicle is running straight, all the wheels should
rotate truly automatically. When the vehicle has to negotiate a
curve or a corner, the steering inner road wheel has to be swivelled
through a larger angle than the outer wheel to maintain true rolling
motion. The *difference* between the two angles has to vary with the
sharpness of the turn, and it must be provided both accurately
and automatically. This is to ensure that each wheel is aligned at
90° to its own radius of turn, i.e. the line between the centre of the
wheel and the centre of the turn. As near as practicable, these differences in swivelling angles are obtained by using the Ackerman
system.

Toe-out on turns

In the Ackerman system the end of the track arm of each stub axle is secured to the end of a transverse track rod, the rod being of such a length that at each side one end lies upon the line between the kingpin and a point on, or near, the pinion nose of the rear axle. The angle formed by these two lines is called the Ackerman angle, and its size is such that when the track rod is moved

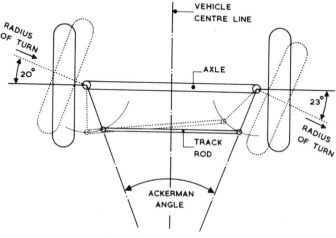

Fig. 9.6 Toe-out on turns

it ceases to remain parallel with the axle, taking up instead a position in which it moves the two track arms and their respective road wheels through the required different angles. The size of the Ackerman angle, and the angular difference at the wheels depends upon the ratio of the vehicle track divided by the wheel base. In the Ackerman system the correct differences are, in fact, only obtained in the straight forward position and in one position in each lock. Slight inaccuracies in all other wheel positions are normally absorbed by slight deflections of the tyres.

While the Ackerman system provides reasonably accurate steering geometry for slow-moving vehicles it has to be modified, by a combination of calculation and experiment, for faster-moving and lighter vehicles. This is because of the effects upon the steering of low-pressure tyres, differences in tyre tread and construction, the distribution of vehicle weight, the softer suspensions, and the effects of centrifugal force and cross winds.

Castor angle

A good steering system will always tend to maintain a straight course and to straighten out, or self centre, automatically after negotiating a corner. This self-centring action has to be overcome by the driver whenever the direction of the vehicle has to be changed. It therefore enables him to 'feel' his steering.

The self-centring effect is usually obtained by tilting the kingpin *backwards at the top*. The angle formed by the projected centre

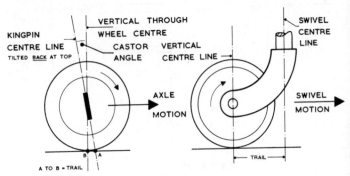

Fig. 9.7 Positive castor

line of the kingpin and the vertical is called the castor angle, and the distance between the two lines at ground level is called castor trail. As the wheel is always being pulled along behind its pivot centre line, it always aligns itself in the direction being taken by the vehicle – centring itself in the same way as a castor of a dinner wagon does.

A steering road wheel which is also a driving wheel will not self centre – unless the kingpin is tilted in the opposite direction, i.e. forwards at the top. This reversal of the conventional angle is known as negative castor angle.

The castor angle varies between vehicles but is usually between 2° and 5°. Too large a castor angle produces steering which is hard to operate; too small a castor angle causes the vehicle to wander, and it may also cause wheel wobble.

The tilting of the kingpin may be obtained in leaf spring and beam axle arrangements by:

(a) Fitting a wedge between the spring and the axle bedplate.
(b) Arranging the spring centre bolt and the axle closer to the forward end of the spring.
(c) Tilting the spring and axle assembly so that the front end of the spring is higher than the rear end.

Where IFS units are employed the whole assembly may be tilted in the original design. In other arrangements adjustments may be made through screwed bushes, or adjustable tie or torque rods, to obtain the same effect.

Centre point steering

When the vehicle is moving, the force acting at the kingpin (to pull the wheel along) has to overcome the resistance of the wheel. If the kingpin and the wheel centre lines were parallel, and at 90° to the axle, these forces would act together (as a couple) to force the wheels to open outward or splay, the splaying effect being very greatly increased when the brakes were applied. In addition the wheel centre, being relatively distant from the kingpin, necessitates the wheel turning through an arc about the kingpin instead of about its own vertical centre line. This results in (a) a considerable effort being needed at the steering wheel and (b) large bending stresses being imposed on the stub axles and kingpins.

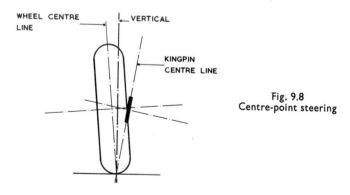

Fig. 9.8
Centre-point steering

Heavy steering, splay, and very high stresses are reduced by, in effect, bringing the wheel and the kingpin centres closer together. This is done by tilting the wheel outwards at the top and the king-pin inwards at the top, reducing the radius of the arc through which the wheel has to swivel. The centre lines projected should meet at ground level; when they do, centre point steering is said to have been obtained. In practice, due to tyre spread, only approximate centre point steering can be obtained.

Camber angle
Wheel camber is obtained by tilting the wheel *outwards at the top*. The camber angle is the angle formed between the centre line of the wheel and the vertical, and it is usually less than 2°. The tilting of the wheel is obtained by inclining the horizontal centre line of the stub axle and results in the wheel describing a smaller arc about the kingpin at road level. This makes the wheel easier to swivel, and camber therefore provides lighter steering. It will also compensate for the effects of road camber and small suspension defects upon the steering.

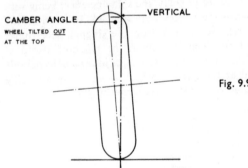

Fig. 9.9. Camber angle

Because the centre line of the stub axle is inclined, the radius of the inner part of the tyre tread is greater than that of the outer part of the tread and this causes the wheel to run out, or splay, when the vehicle is moving. This splay action must be controlled by the track rod, which is therefore under compressive stress if fitted behind the axle, or under tensile stress if fitted in front of the axle. The difference between the radii also results in the inner bearing, which can easily be made the larger, being subjected to the heavier supporting load.

Under normal conditions, the effect upon the steering of the splay action of one wheel is counteracted or balanced by the splay action of the opposite wheel – and the vehicle will run straight. If the camber angle at one side is greater than that at the other side the vehicle will pull over to the side having the greater camber angle. Due to the much greater splay forces, excessively large camber angles increase the wear on tyres and ball pin joints, and the stress on the track rod. The splay action is easily demonstrated by disconnecting one ball joint of the track rod and pushing the vehicle forward. Both wheels will immediately splay and prevent further movement of the vehicle.

Kingpin inclination angle

The kingpin is tilted *inwards at the top* to assist in obtaining centre-point steering without excessive camber, i.e. assists the camber angle. The angle between the centre line of the kingpin and the vertical is known as the kingpin inclination angle (k.p.i.) and this is usually between 5° and 10°. The modern tendency is towards wheels of smaller diameter and, because it is essential to keep the camber angle small, the reduction of wheel diameter accompanies the use of larger kingpin inclination angles. Larger angles may also be used where longer stub axles are needed to permit the use of wider hub assemblies.

When the stub axle is moved from lock to lock, its end, due to the inclination of the kingpin, follows a curved path in the vertical

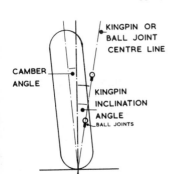

Fig. 9.10 Kingpin inclination

plane. This results in the front end of the vehicle being lifted slightly as the wheels swivel towards full lock. The weight of the front end therefore helps to return the wheels to the straight forward position, i.e. kingpin inclination also has self-centring action.

The effects of the combined use of camber and kingpin inclination are to:

(a) Provide easier steering.
(b) Reduce the effect of braking upon the steering.
(c) Provide a self-centring effect.
(d) Reduce stress, and even out the load upon the wheel bearings.

The sizes of the camber and kingpin inclination angles may be reduced slightly by employing dished wheels, the dishing allowing the wheel and tyre centre line to be brought closer to the kingpin centre line.

Toe-in

The road wheels of a vehicle should always rotate with a true rolling motion, i.e. be parallel when the vehicle is following a straight path. The use of camber angle, however, results in the opening out of the front wheels. This is possible due to the inevitable 'give' in the steering linkages and ball joints. As this splaying action causes excessive tyre and wheel-bearing wear it is counteracted by pointing the wheels in (toeing-in) when the vehicle is at rest. In this way, although the wheels still splay out, they become parallel when running.

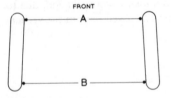

Fig. 9.11
Toe-in (toe-in = distance B minus A)

The toe-in of the wheels is the difference in the distances between the wheel rims or tyre tread centres, measured at stub axle height, behind and in front of the axle. Toe-in is usually between 0·8 mm and 4·8 mm and, as toe-in is necessary because of the use of camber, toe-in must be increased as the camber angle is increased. In vehicles with front-wheel drive the wheels tend to run in, so toe-out is used instead of toe-in. The adjustment in or out is carried out by altering the length of the track rod(s) and is a trial-and-error process. As in all checks on steering geometry, the wheel rims must first be examined for run-out and a buckled rim must be taken into account.

Beam axle checking

In commercial vehicles, where beam axles are still widely used, the steering geometry can be checked in the same ways, and by using the same gauges, as those for IFS suspension arrangements. Apart from toe-in, no adjustments are possible, rectification being carried out by the cold bending of the axle to re-align the kingpin bore angles with the spring bedplates, and with the stub axle centre lines. Generally it is better to send such axles to the specialist repairer or manufacturer; severe bending will require heating which will destroy the original heat treatment – and this must be properly restored or the axle will be either too soft or too brittle.

The axle should be placed in a vice and one spring bedplate should be set horizontal with the aid of a spirit level or a combination square. The two plates must be parallel when viewed from the end, and this is checked by using the level on the opposite bedplate. Each kingpin inclination angle may be checked by fitting into its bore an arbor bar centralized by two cones. At the top of the bar a weighted, free-swinging pointer moves over a small centre-zero protractor scale to indicate the angle. Both sides should be at the same angle. If the castor angle is obtained by tilting the kingpin in relation to the bedplates (instead of by the axle position on the spring) this may be checked by turning the gauge and the pointer through 90°.

WHEEL ALIGNMENT CHECKING

Precautions

The following should be examined and, if necessary, corrected before carrying out steering geometry checks:

(a) All tyres for their correct pressures.
(b) Tyres for tread depth and evidence of faulty wheel geometry.
(c) Hub bearings for correct adjustment and free play.
(d) Kingpins and bushes for excessive wear and lift.
(e) Ball pin joints for excessive wear, locking, and rod lift.

(f) Swivel points of suspension unit for excessive free movement.
(g) Shackle pins and bushes for excessive wear and side movement.
(h) Spring U bolts for tightness and plate security.
(i) Steering gearbox for excessive wear and whether secure on chassis.

The vehicle should always be placed upon a smooth and level floor or upon levelled steel plates.

Toe-in checking

There are three main ways of checking toe-in or toe-out. The first uses some form of trammel, the second a trammel and an optical system of measurement, and the third a track indicator to give a reading from the side thrust of a rotating wheel and tyre.

Trammel method. The trammel may be made in the workshop or obtained from manufacturers of garage equipment. Its purpose is to compare distances, not to measure them. It must be adjustable to suit different widths of vehicle track, and different heights of stub axle. Allowances must be made for slightly buckled wheel rims. The vehicle is placed upon a flat floor with the front wheels in line with the rear wheels. The trammel is set up behind the wheels, with the two points or arms adjusted to the height of the stub axle ends. Each tyre tread is marked with chalk at this height and the points are set on to, and marking, the centre of each tread. The trammel is then removed and the vehicle pushed or driven forward to rotate the wheels through 180°. The trammel is now positioned in front of the wheels with one point on one centre mark of the tread. The difference between the other point and the tread centre mark is the toe-in or toe-out. This must be compared with the figure specified by the vehicle manufacturer and, if found to be incorrect, the length of the track rod must be adjusted to bring the actual toe-in within the limits specified.

The Churchill 96 track gauge (see Plate 1) is an example of an improved type of trammel. In this instrument one point or probe is linked to a pointer which moves over a scale to indicate the degree of toe-in or toe-out. The scale may be turned about and so makes possible measurements in British or metric units. The probes are specially designed to provide readings which are consistently accurate. The trammel bar is telescopic, and has a coarse adjustment (by the handle) and a fine adjustment (by the knob) for setting the pointer to zero. In use the probes are set to axle height in front of the wheels and at the side wall centres of the tyres. The trammel length is adjusted as this is done and the pointer is set to zero on the scale by turning the knob. The gauge is then removed and the vehicle rolled forward for half a wheel revolution. When the gauge is refitted the pointer indicates the toe-in or toe-out. Adjustments may be made with the gauge in position.

Optical method. In this a longitudinal trammel is placed against each front wheel, with the two arms contacting each side of the wheel rim. The two trammels extend forward of the wheels and one is fitted with a longitudinally arranged mirror. The other trammel is fitted with a long, vertical, viewing tube at the lower end of which, and facing the mirror, is a fine vertical line and a reflector plate. When using the equipment, the mechanic looks through the view tube and sees the vertical line of the tube, and lines reflected by the mirror. The tube is gently turned until the view tube line is centralized with the reflected lines and in this position a pointer, attached to the tube, indicates the toe-in or toe-out on a scale secured to the trammel. The scale is calibrated to read run-out in metres per kilometre, and a conversion can be made to read in fractions of a millimetre.

Track indicator. This consists of a long metal plate with a ramp at each end. The plate is attached to its base through a system of levers and longitudinal rollers, a scale and a carrying handle being arranged at the centre of one side of the base. Any transverse movement of the plate is magnified and indicated on the scale by a pointer. One wheel at a time is checked with the indicator. The vehicle must be pushed or driven slowly over the plate; any sidewards motion of the tyre, due to toe-in or toe-out, results in the plate moving sideways and this movement is indicated by the pointer. The effect of the side force may be read off in m/km or in mm, and is given as toe-in or toe-out. Readings should be taken as the wheel passes over the centre of the plate. It is important that the indicator be used only on a smooth and level floor, and that the wheel be passed over the plate twice before a reading is taken. Track-rod adjustments can be made while the wheel is on the plate, this feature being particularly useful where two- or three-piece track rods are fitted.

CHECKING CAMBER, CASTOR AND KINGPIN INCLINATION

A large number of different gauges have been devised for checking these angles and each has its own special instructions for use, which must be adhered to, and its own ancillary equipment. Normally measurements accurate to $\frac{1}{4}°$ can be obtained. The mechanic is urged to learn the correct use of more than one manufacturer's equipment.

The Churchill steering alignment gauge (see Plate 2) has three main components, i.e. two turntables and the gauge assembly. The turntables consist of a strong, square, base plate with a carrying handle. A heavy steel disc with a pointer is attached to the base and can swivel upon it on ball bearings. The pointer moves over an adjustable scale which is calibrated to read up to 25° on each side of a central zero.

The gauge assembly consists of one, or two, cylindrical shafts which are attached at their lower end to a flat-edged and rigid foot. The foot is at 90° to the shaft and is long enough to contact both sides of the tyre. At the centre of the shafts is a quadrant-shaped body consisting of a sliding block arranged between two fixed blocks. The sliding block carries a spirit level and has an indicator mark at each side of the level, the marks coinciding with degree scales attached to the fixed blocks. The scale nearest the shaft is a centre-zero type indicating the degrees of camber, while the scale on the other block indicates castor and kingpin inclination angles when the wheel is swivelled through 20°. The body can be swivelled on the shaft and is automatically located when the scales are either parallel with, or at 90° to, the plane of the wheel. At the top of the shaft is an off-set foot which is clamped to the shaft in a position suited to the diameter of the wheel. In use the gauge assembly is held to the wheel by wire clips and springs, or by a three-point cam action.

Setting up

When steering angles are to be checked, the precautions listed earlier must always be carried out. The vehicle is placed on a smooth and level floor with the front wheel in the straight forward position. The turntables are placed centrally in front of the wheels and are set to zero after centralizing the adjustable scales on the

Plate 1. Churchill 96 track gauge

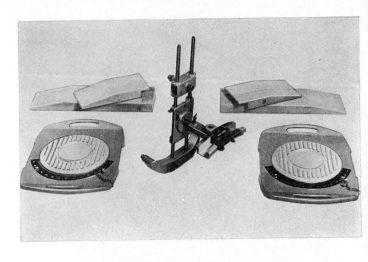

Plate 2. Churchill 121 wheel alignment equipment

base plates. The vehicle is then pushed or driven forward to bring the front wheels to the centres of the turntables. The brakes are applied and those of the front wheels locked on. For greater accuracy blocks of the same height as the turntables should be placed under the rear wheels. The adjustable scales of the turntables are now moved carefully to read zero and are clamped.

Camber check

In this operation the turntables are not used. The gauge is offered up to the wheel and the off-set foot is adjusted and clamped on the shaft to give a three-point contact on the tyre. The gauge is then held in position by the wire clips and springs, or by the cam action. The body is so positioned on the shaft that the scales are parallel with the wheel, and the sliding block is moved to align its mark with the zero of the camber scale. The whole gauge assembly is then moved gently on the wheel until the spirit level bubble is centralized on its marks. At this point the shaft has been set vertical in the plane of the wheel, i.e. as seen from the side.

The body is now swivelled on the shaft through 90° and the bubble is again centralized – this time by moving the sliding block. As seen from the front, this brings the sliding block and its marks into the vertical plane while the shaft and the scales are in the tilted plane of the wheel. The number of degrees of camber on the wheel can now be read from the scale at the point which coincides with the mark of the sliding block.

Castor check

The turntables are required for this operation and must be carefully zeroed. The gauge unit is set to zero as in the camber check, i.e. with the scales parallel with the wheel, the sliding block mark on the camber scale zero, and the bubble centralized on its marks.

The wheel is now swivelled outwards until the turntable indicates 20°. The gauge *body is turned through 90°* and the bubble centralized on its marks by moving the sliding block. The reading of the castor, kingpin inclination scale should now be noted.

The wheel is then swivelled inwards to read 20° on the turntable, the bubble centralized again, and the scale read. The *difference* between the two readings of the scale is the castor angle in degrees.

Kingpin inclination check

The wheel is swivelled outwards through 20° and the *body* of the gauge is *set parallel with the wheel.* The spirit level bubble is then centralized and the castor, kingpin inclination scale read. The wheel is then turned inwards to the 20° position on the turntable and the scale again read. The *difference* between the two readings is the kingpin inclination angle in degrees.

Optical checking

The modern tendency toward faster servicing leads to the setting up of workshop bays or areas in which one type of work only is carried out. These bays are fully equipped with all the necessary tools, instruments, gauges, and supplies for the work to be done, and are manned by mechanics who rapidly become expert in the operations involved. Steering geometry checks and adjustments may be made under this system and optical methods may replace the existing mechanical methods.

In most of these systems a specially designed, low-voltage lamp is secured to the centre of each front wheel. The lamps project a shadow of crossed lines upon a screen or screens set up vertically in front of the vehicle. The screens are marked out for the various steering geometry angles, and basic setting points, and the readings are taken from the point where the shadow lines intersect on a marking on the screen scale. One form of optical checking equipment is the Churchill 122 × Optoflex shown in Plate 3, page 204.

Adjustments

In most vehicles, adjustments cannot be made to correct steering angles found different from those specified by their manufacturers. Rectification work consists of locating and replacing bent or damaged parts by new ones. Steering parts should never be heated and bent back into shape, because the effects of their original heat treatment will be destroyed – thus making the part a source of danger. Cold bending by the use of hydraulic rams may be allowed as a temporary measure until new parts are obtained.

There are a few independent suspension arrangements in which the camber angle may be adjusted by the use of shims. These are fitted between the chassis and the upper wishbone mountings, thicker shimming increasing the angle and vice versa. In a very few designs castor angle may be adjusted by screwed bushes.

10

Wheels and Tyres

WHEELS

Vehicle road wheels must be strong but light in weight. They must be easy to remove and refit, and should be easy to clean. Two main types of wheel in service are the wire or spoked wheel and the pressed steel or ventilated disc wheel.

Wire wheels

Wire wheels are now used only on sports and racing cars because they are much more expensive to produce and maintain than the disc type. They are lighter in weight than disc types, and it is easier to cool the wheel and the brake assembly. (See Illustration.)

Wire wheel and bolt-detachable wheel

The rims are connected to the hubs by two or three rows of steel spokes, their tension being adjustable to maintain the rim in its correct position relative to the hub. The spokes are arranged tangentially and in opposition to each other to enable them to resist the driving and braking torques. Under suspension load the upper spokes are in tension.

The hub of the wheel may be secured to the hub on the axle by four or six studs and cone-ended nuts, or by means of one large 'knock-on' central nut. In the latter method the outside of the axle hub and the inside of the wheel hub are splined, and the wheel is centralized by conical faces at each side – one being on the nut. The nut is hammered tight with a bronze hammer and left- and right-handed threads are used.

Disc wheels

These consist of a pressed steel disc to which the steel rim is riveted or welded. The disc is dished and has radially arranged slots under the rim to allow air to circulate and cool the wheel and the brake drums. Ventilated disc wheels may consist of up to four separate parts, varying with the type of vehicle and the method of attaching the tyre. The most common type for cars and light commercial vehicles is the one-piece wheel with well-base rim. (See Illustration.)

Well-base rim

The bead of a tyre is made up from twisted wire loops – which cannot be stretched during fitting and removal operations. The rims must therefore be so designed as to allow the tyre to be held firmly in place yet be simple to remove. In the well-base, or drop-centre, types of rim, the side of each bead is held by a flange while its inner edge is forced, by the air pressure, outwards and up a small tapered face – the wedging action locking the tyre to the rim. When the tyre is to be removed the rear bead must be forced down into the well to enable the outer bead to be levered over the edge of the flange.

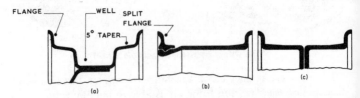

Fig. 10.1 Rims: (a) well base; (b) flat base; (c) divided

Flat base rim

These types are used for the heavier commercial vehicles. The rim base is flat and has one fixed and one detachable flange. The latter is located on the base and is secured to it by a large, split, lock ring which fits into recesses in both the flange and the rim.

In another type, used by the medium range of commercial vehicles, the flange and the lock ring are combined and fit into a special shape of recess formed in the outer edge of the rim. This type may also have a small well and a slight bead lock taper.

Military, and some special-purpose vehicles, are fitted with divided rim wheels. In these the disc and half the rim are made as one piece, the other half of the rim being bolted to the disc. These types therefore have two rings of nuts, and it is most important that the rim nuts are not removed by mistake when removing the wheel. The rim nuts are the outer ring and are often painted red as a warning not to release them.

In all these types the tyre should always be inflated with the wheel behind a strong steel guard – a lock ring which flies off may cripple or kill someone nearby.

The wheels in these types are secured to the hubs by studs and cone-ended nuts, the nut cones engaging with cones formed in the wheel disc to centralize the wheel upon the hub. It is important that the wheel nuts be kept tight and that they are tightened down in a diagonal sequence.

In many Continental designs the rim is bolted to wide spokes or to a disc permanently attached to the axle hub. This arrangement may also be employed in some agricultural vehicles where a different width of track may be needed – and can be obtained by reversing the rim and tyre on their hub.

TYRES

In motor vehicles the tyre is used to increase the riding comfort. Perhaps of even greater importance nowadays is the fact that the tyre greatly increases the grip of the wheels upon the road under widely varying operating conditions. Essentially the tyre is a flexible casing which contains air, the air absorbing shock and vibration. Modern types include both tubed and tubeless tyres.

Tubed tyre

This is an assembly of a cover, or casing, and an inner air tube. The cover must be strong, light in weight, and flexible. It must resist wear at the tread and maintain a good grip upon the road under many different conditions. It must also grip the wheel rim, resist the pressure exerted by the air in the inner tube, and be able to withstand the heat resulting from friction and its own flexing during use.

Tyre manufacture (see Plate 4)

In manufacture, a length of thin rubber sheet is wound over a metal drum and its ends joined by a rubber cement. Over this are wound layers or plies of rayon or nylon cords impregnated with rubber reinforced by carbon black. The cords in each ply are parallel with each other but are angled in relation to the drum. Alternate plies are arranged so that their cords cross (hence cross-ply construction) to provide a stronger and more flexible case. The number of plies and their crossing angle help to determine the characteristics of the tyre. Inextensible twisted wire loops are then fitted at each side of the drum and the ply edges turned over them and cemented to form the beads. The number of plies is increased as the intended maximum load is increased, ranging from a four-ply rating to a twenty-ply rating for the larger vehicles.

A strip of cushioning rubber is cemented over the casing and a chafer strip is cemented over the beads. Over all these is cemented a tougher rubber under-tread, and then a thicker layer of yet tougher rubber. The cylindrical assembly is then removed from the drum and placed into a moulding press in which heat and pressure are applied. These cure or bond the various rubber components together and toughen up the rubber as the final shapes of the side walls and tread are formed.

The inner tube is made from natural or synthetic rubber and must be air-tight and flexible. It is fitted with a valve for inflation and pressure regulation.

Valve detail

The valve assembly is contained in a hollow brass tube. In commercial vehicles this tube can be long and cranked, and is bonded into a rubber case or footing, the whole being cured to the inner

Plate 3. Churchill 122X Optoflex

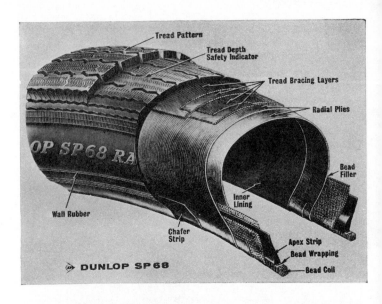

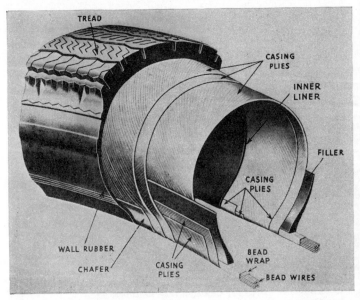

Plate 4. Construction of radial-ply tyre (top) and cross-ply tyre

tube. On the smaller vehicles the tube is bonded into an 'all cover' rubber body which may be vulcanized to an inner tube or, on tubeless wheels, be an air-tight fit in a hole through the wheel rim. The valve tube is threaded internally and externally at its outer end and is protected from the entry of dirt by a screwed sealing cap which also acts as a secondary air seal. Below the internal threads is a conical sealing face and at the inner end is a shoulder.

The valve assembly consists of a centre pin which has an integral metal and rubber disc valve. The pin and the disc valve are

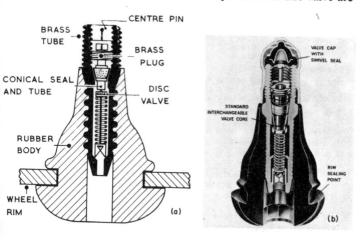

Fig. 10.2 Tubeless tyre valve (a) principles of construction; (b) sectional view of Schrader valve

spring loaded to move outwards but are restrained by a small tube with an external Teflon conical seal and a hollow, screwed, brass plug. When the valve assembly is installed, by screwing down the brass plug with a forked key, the conical Teflon seal makes a semi-permanent air-tight joint with the inner conical face of the tube. The bottom end of the seal tube is made air-tight by the spring-loaded disc valve.

When the tyre inflator is fitted to the valve tube, the centre pin is depressed, and the disc valve is forced away from the bottom of the seal tube to allow compressed air to enter the tyre or the

inner tube. When the inflator is removed, the spring forces the
disc valve to seal the end of the seal tube, the spring force and the
pressure difference acting to retain the pressure. If the pressure is
too high it may be reduced by depressing the pin. If all the air is
to be released the valve assembly can be completely removed from
the valve tube.

Balanced tubes
Both tube and tyre may be tested for balance by the manufacturer,
the lighter side of the tyre and the heavier side of the tube being
marked by dots. The two sets of dots should be together to obtain
the best balance of the assembly.

Tubeless tyres
This type has now replaced the tubed type for most cars and
smaller commercial vehicles. It has the following advantages:
(1) It is lighter in weight.
(2) It runs at lower temperature.
(3) It holds its pressure longer.
(4) It is easier to service.
(5) It is less likely to cause roadside stoppages for punctures.
    The main disadvantages are that a tourniquet is usually required
when inflating, and that the rim must be air-tight. It is not therefore suitable for the normal type of spoked wheel.
    The construction of tubed and tubeless tyres is generally similar,
but in the tubeless type the inner tube is replaced by an extra layer
of soft rubber. This lines the casing and covers the beads to ensure
an air-tight seal at the rim. The beads are wider and the locking
taper on the rim is about 15° instead of 5°. Tubeless tyres should
not therefore be fitted to wheels not designed for them. Both types
of tyre can be remoulded, and both *must* be vulcanized in repair.
Plugs in tubeless tyres are only a temporary repair – until vulcanized the tyre will be very dangerous to use at high speeds.

Radial-ply tyres (see Plate 10)
    In these tyres the cords of the plies do not cross but are arranged
radially, i.e. at 90° to the tangents of the wheel. A fairly stiff
bracing of textile or steel cords is also fitted under the tread and
the tyres are classified as radial textile or radial steel. Radial tyres

have much improved road-gripping qualities and operate at lower temperatures than cross-ply tyres. They provide a harder ride at speeds of under about 60 km/h because the tread bracing reduces their deflection, but at higher speeds they have a higher deflection which increases comfort and road holding.

Tyre mixing
The recommendations of the vehicle and tyre manufacturers must be adhered to; indiscriminate mixing of tyres of different construction and characteristics can lead to serious accidents. Radial-ply tyres generate very high cornering forces and grip the road firmly. Generally cross-ply tyres may be used at the front with radials at the rear, the radials promoting understeer, which is not dangerous. If this arrangement is reversed, oversteer, which can be very dangerous indeed, will result. Similarly radial-textile tyres may be used at the front with radial-steel tyres at the rear – but not vice versa. Tyres of the same type and tread should always be fitted on any one axle.

Tyre rating
Tyres are classified by sizes and ply ratings, and these are related to their inflation pressures and the maximum load to be imposed upon them. These figures are made available by the tyre manufacturers and enable the vehicle designers to select the most suitable tyres for a particular vehicle. The figures of most interest to the mechanic are those of size and pressure, the size being given as the nominal width of cross-section and the radius of the wheel, e.g. 5.60×15 means that the cross-sectional diameter is about 5·6 in and the wheel radius is 15 in. An example of a commercial tyre may be 7.00×20 (10-ply rating). At a pressure of 276 kN/m² the maximum weight should not exceed 840 kg, the weight limit being increased by approximately 50 kg for each extra 35 kN/m² up to a maximum of 520 kN/m². Radial tyres are given in mm and cross-ply in inches at the time of writing.

Aquaplaning
This is the name given to the highly dangerous fault in which the tyre tread fails to clear away the water in front of each segment as it contacts the ground. A wedge of water builds up in front of the segments and finally forces them clear of the road surface. This

occurs at the non-driving wheels and the vehicle then fails to respond to the steering and the brakes. Modern tyres with slotted treads will seldom be affected by this fault, even at high speeds on very wet roads. This is because the slots act like a squeegee and push the water away from the segments. Where high tyre pressures and smooth treads occur together, aquaplaning can take place at relatively low speeds.

Care of tyres
To obtain the maximum life from a set of tyres the following points should be observed:

(1) Regular inspection of tyres for nails, stones, etc. These should be removed and any small cuts or abrasions repaired by vulcanizing. Large cuts and more extensive damage, especially to the larger and more expensive tyres, should be dealt with by the specialist repairer.

(2) Inflation pressures must be maintained at the recommended values. Under-inflation causes excessive tension in the walls and this fractures the cords of the plies, making even a new tyre dangerous. Under-inflation is indicated when the outsides of the tread show more wear than the centre. Low-pressure tyres demand particular care with their pressure maintenance. Over-inflation, due to the increased stress, results in extra wear at the centre of the tread and may result in a burst at some point weakened by a previous impact load. It also reduces comfort, and increases shock and vibration throughout the vehicle.

(3) To ensure uniform wear, particularly where independent suspension is used, the wheels should be changed around at about 5000 km intervals – bringing the spare wheel into circulation, e.g. spare to rear offside; rear o/s to front near side; front n/s to rear n/s; rear n/s to front o/s; front o/s to spare.

(4) Toe-in or toe-out must be kept within the specified limits. Excessive toe-in will cause the outer portions of the tread of each front wheel to wear more rapidly than the inner portions. Excessive toe-out has the reverse effect.

(5) Excessive camber angle will result in excessive tyre wear, the outer edges of each tread rib being worn more than the inner – giving a saw-tooth effect.

(6) Mechanical damage to the wheels, steering, suspension, or chassis alignment which results in the mis-alignment of the wheels.

(7) The use of the clutch and the brakes. The too violent use of either of these may result in the formation of flats on the treads and/or damage to the plies through sudden over-loading.

(8) Impact loads. These may be due to bad driving or poor roads, the impact weakening or breaking the cords and leading to a later burst.

(9) Oil, grease and paint should never be left on tyres as they weaken or destroy the rubber.

(10) Continuous exposure to the ultra violet light in strong sunshine will cause a hardening and cracking of the rubber. Always store tyres in cool and indirectly lit places.

WHEEL BALANCING

Modern cars are very sensitive to the balance of their wheels. Wheels should be checked for correct balance at about 10 000 km intervals, and after removal and refitting, and repair. Out-of-balance front wheels may cause wheel tramp or wobble, out-of-balance rear wheels may cause a vibration so similar to a transmission vibration that it is difficult to locate.

Static balance

When a wheel is allowed to turn freely, and one part of it always comes to rest at the bottom, the wheel is said to be statically out of balance. This is readily seen in a bicycle wheel where the valve always comes to rest at the bottom. The part which comes to the bottom is of course the heaviest part, and if the wheel is rotated at a high speed, centrifugal force, acting through this heaviest part, will cause the wheel to leave the ground each time the heaviest part comes to the top. This fault is known as wheel tramp, or hop, or patter, and it may be corrected by fitting a small weight to the wheel diametrically opposite the heaviest part. The size of the weight must be determined by experiment. When the wheel will stay in any position, and it is free from tramp, it is said to be in static (low speed) balance.

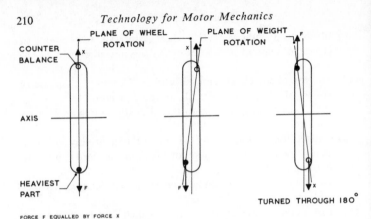

FORCE F EQUALLED BY FORCE X

Fig. 10.3 Static (low speed) balance

Dynamic balance

A wheel may be balanced statically but still cause violent wheel movements at *high speeds*. This is because the heaviest part is to one side of, and not on, the centre plane of the wheel. The action of centrifugal force, through the off-centre heaviest part, causes the wheel to pivot left and right, and in and out, as it rotates. This violent and uncontrollable movement is known as wheel wobble

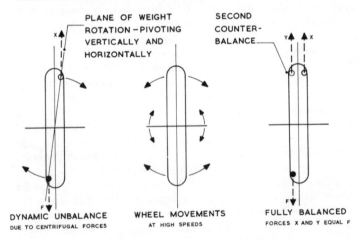

Fig. 10.4 Dynamic (high speed) balance

or shimmy and, because it occurs at high road speeds, it is particularly dangerous. The wheel involved is said to be dynamically
unbalanced. Dynamic unbalance can also be corrected by fitting
opposing weights but determining the position and size of the
weights means using special testing and balancing equipment upon
which the wheel can be rotated at high speeds. When the wheel can
be rotated at high speeds and it is free from vibration it is said to
be dynamically balanced.

Balancing

A number of different wheel-balancing machines are available.
Static and dynamic balancing are usually done on the same
machine and as part of the same operation. In some machines the
wheel is removed from the vehicle, while in others the wheel is
balanced on its own hub.

In the Weaver wheel balancer the wheel is secured to one end
of a spindle driven, through a clutch, by an electric motor. The

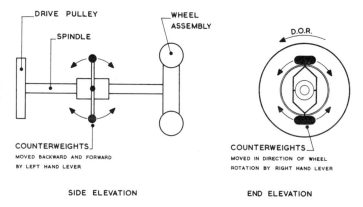

SIDE ELEVATION   END ELEVATION

Fig. 10.5 Wheel balancer

spindle is mounted in such a way that it is free to move under the
influence of any unbalanced forces which may be acting upon the
wheel, the movements or vibrations being shown by an indicator.
Two opposed counterweights are mounted upon the spindle. These
can be tilted forward and backward by a lever on the left-hand side

of the machine, and around the spindle in its direction of rotation by a lever on the right-hand side.

The wheel is first balanced statically by a counterweight. The drive clutch is then engaged and the spindle and the wheel are driven at a high speed. The two levers are then moved carefully until the indicator shows there is no vibration affecting the spindle. The drive is then stopped and balance weights are clipped to the inner and outer sides of the wheel rim where indicated by the counterbalance positions. The sizes of the weights, in grams, are given by the lever positions in their quadrants.

11

The Braking System

Advantages

Hydraulic or fluid-operated brake systems have almost completely replaced the older cable or rod-operated systems because they have the following advantages:

(1) Compensation is automatic because the pressure in an *enclosed* system is the same at all points in the system.

(2) In the design stage the force derived from the pressure can be made larger or smaller by simply altering the area of a particular piston face and bore.

(3) There is no lost motion and reduction of force due to wear and lever angularity.

(4) The use of independent suspension does not unduly complicate the design and operation of the braking system.

Where larger forces are required than can reasonably be obtained by direct pedal thrust, a vacuum or compressed-air servo unit may be fitted. These units are arranged between the master cylinder and the wheel cylinders and they operate by increasing the pressure of the fluid. In large commercial vehicles the system may be of the continuous-flow type in which pressure is provided by a gearbox or engine-driven pump.

Brake systems are all designed to make retardation directly proportional to the forces applied at the pedal. This is to enable the driver to 'feel' his braking.

There must also be an independently operated system which can apply the brakes of at least two wheels when the vehicle is parked. This legal requirement is usually met by the inclusion of a cable or rod system which can apply the rear brakes without affecting the fluid system.

System layout

The system consists of a fluid tank or reservoir, a master cylinder, a system of rigid and flexible pipes, pipe junctions, and wheel cylinder assemblies. The reservoir may be combined with the master cylinder. The wheel cylinders may operate shoes and linings or disc pads. A pressure-operated switch, which controls the brake warning lamps, is usually fitted at the first junction from the master cylinder.

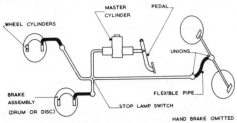

Fig. 11.1 Lockheed fluid brake system (hand brake omitted)

In the Lockheed system a spring-loaded check valve is used to maintain a minimum pressure of about 55 kN/m^2 in the pipe lines and wheel cylinders. The purpose of this residual or standing pressure is to:

(1) Enable the shoes or pads to move out to contact the drums or discs the moment the pedal is depressed.
(2) Ensure that any leakage is of fluid escaping (which is easy to detect) and is not of air entering (which is very hard to locate and which makes the brakes unreliable and dangerous).

The Girling system does not employ a standing pressure.

Brake fluid

The fluid used in hydraulic brake systems is a vegetable oil with certain additives. It must:

(a) Have a low freezing point.
(b) Have a high boiling point.
(c) Have low viscosity under a wide range of temperatures.
(d) Not attack the rubber and metal parts of the system.
(e) Not deteriorate except over a long period of service.

It is most important that only the correct make and type of fluid be used in a particular system. Apart from the automatic cancellation of manufacturers' guarantees, the mixing of different fluids may result in chemical actions taking place which partly solidify the fluid, or which produce materials which attack and destroy the rubber parts of the system.

Fluid contamination

It is even more important that engine oil, shock absorber oil, petrol, and paraffin *NEVER* be introduced into a fluid brake system – nor should they ever be used to clean brake parts. The use of these mineral-based oils results in the rapid weakening or destruction of all the rubber components, and possibly in the injury or death of the vehicle users. Cleaning should always be done with industrial methylated spirit, followed by washing in clean brake fluid and/or application of the correct rubber grease. A system contaminated by mineral oils or wrong fluids must be thoroughly flushed out with methylated spirit, the contaminated fluid destroyed at once, and all rubber parts (including flexible pipes) replaced. Flushing is similar to normal bleeding except that the fluid is replaced by methylated spirit, and at least a litre of spirit passed through each bleed valve. Flushing should be carried out once every three years of normal service, and whenever the fluid appears thick and dirty.

Working precautions

(1) All equipment used for brake system work must be clean and free from traces of mineral oil. Keep hands and tools clean.
(2) Fluid system parts must be cleaned only with the correct cleaning fluid or industrial methylated spirits.
(3) Use only the correct make and grade of fluid.
(4) Never re-use fluid from a system. It may be contaminated or dirty. Brake fluids absorb water and old fluid will contain some.
(5) Fill dust seals with rubber grease during service work and always replace bleed nipple caps.
(6) Inspect the fluid level in the reservoir at regular intervals and top up as required with the correct fluid.
(7) Replace shoes when their linings are worn down to the rivets or when bonded linings are worn to within 1·5 mm of the shoe.

DRUM BRAKES

In these types the shoes and their operating and adjusting mechanisms are enclosed by a drum which rotates with the wheel, and are mounted upon a circular backplate bolted rigidly to either a front stub axle or the rear axle case.

Leading shoe

Where the expander forces a shoe outwards in the same direction as the rotation of the drum the resulting friction causes the shoe to force itself harder against the drum, i.e. the shoe has a self-applying or self-servo action. Such a shoe is called a leading shoe and, in a leading and trailing shoe assembly, the leading shoe provides about three-quarters of the total retarding force.

Trailing shoe

Where the expander forces a shoe outwards in the opposite direction from the rotation of the drum the resulting friction forces the shoe away from the drum. This is called a trailing shoe. Such shoes provide only about one-quarter of the total retarding force of the leading and trailing shoe assembly.

Two different shoe assemblies may be used. These are:

(1) The leading-and-trailing shoe assembly (L&T).
(2) The two-leading shoe assembly (2LS).

LEADING-AND-TRAILING-SHOE ASSEMBLIES

In these arrangements both shoes, in effect, pivot about the same point and a single expander unit forces the other ends of the shoes outwards in opposite directions. Although the pedal travel stays fairly constant under severe usage, and the retardation or stopping power is not greatly reduced by *small* quantities of oil or water on the linings, this arrangement does require much larger forces at the pedal than are needed by two-leading-shoe arrangements. It has the advantage that the same stopping power is available in both directions of wheel rotation, and it lends itself more easily to the incorporation of both mechanical and fluid methods of operation. For these reasons the leading-and-trailing shoe arrangement is often used for the rear wheel brakes.

Lockheed rear brake

The two shoes are both held in position by a slotted and rigidly mounted anchor plate which transmits the torque reaction forces from the shoes to the backplate and the rear axle case. A single operating cylinder is fitted between the ends of the shoes diametrically opposite the anchor plate and slightly below the rear axle. The cylinder is free to slide in a slot cut in the backplate. Two

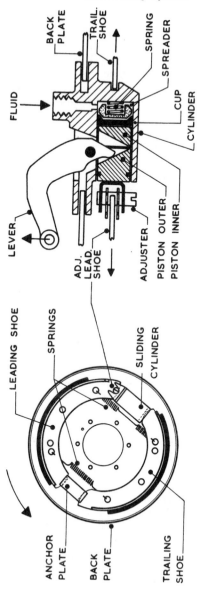

Fig. 11.3 Lockheed operating cylinder

Fig. 11. 2 Lockheed rear brake

different springs are used to hold the shoes to the anchor and to the backplate, the single coil spring being fitted across the anchored ends of the shoes.

The cylinder is an aluminium-alloy casting and has one end sealed. This end is slotted to locate the moving end of the trailing shoe. The cylinder contains a piston, a rubber cup, a plastic cup spreader, and a small spring. The piston is made in two halves, the inner half having a flat face which is sealed by the rubber cup. The outer half carries a metal dust excluder and is slotted to support a 'Micram' adjuster. A pivoted lever, operated by the hand brake, is arranged so that its shorter end fits between the two halves of the piston, the inner faces being slotted for this purpose. As the lever and its pivot are exposed to the rear of the backplate they are enclosed by a rubber boot. The cylinder has a bleed nipple.

Fluid operation

When the pedal is depressed the fluid pressure forces the piston inner half, the end of the lever, and the piston outer half to move outwards and force the leading shoe to contact the drum. At the moment contact is made the reaction force causes the cylinder to move back in its slot and so apply the trailing shoe. The movement of the cylinder in this way divides the available force equally between the two shoes.

Hand-brake operation

When the hand-brake is applied the lever is turned about its pivot and its shorter end forces the piston outer half to move out and apply the leading shoe – without affecting the piston inner half and the fluid system in any way. As the leading shoe contacts the drum the reaction force causes the cylinder to move on the backplate to apply the trailing shoe.

Shoe adjustment

During the normal life of the brakes the clearance between the shoe assemblies and the drum increases as a result of lining wear. This increased clearance is one of the causes of excessive pedal travel, and the clearance must be reduced to the minimum by the use of the shoe adjusters. These reset the shoe position in relation to the drum when the pedal is in the 'off' position.

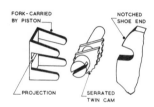

Fig. 11.4
Lockheed Micram adjuster

In Lockheed brakes the adjuster is in the form of a cam, the turning of which forces the moving end of the shoe closer to the drum. The cam consists of a small, solid steel cylinder which has integral twin cams arranged at right angles to its axis. The cylinder fits into the notch in the end of the shoe, and is supported and located in a double fork mounted on the end of the operating piston. One end of the cylinder is either slotted for screwdriver turning or squared for spanner turning. Cam turning due to vibration is prevented by the serration of the cam edges, the serrations being forced to engage with a projection in the base of the fork by the action of the shoe pull-off springs. The spacing of the serrations is such that the correct shoe-to-drum clearance is obtained automatically.

Girling rear brake
The most common types are the hydraulic wedge (HW), and the

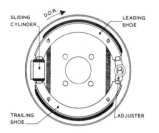

Fig. 11.5
Girling hydraulic-wedge rear brake

hydraulic lever (HL1 and HL3). These types have a rigidly mounted adjuster of the screwed wedge and tappet type but they vary in their types of expander, and in the arrangement of shoe pull-off springs and shoe steadies.

Hydraulic wedge

In these types a single-wheel cylinder, fitted with a bleed nipple, is used. The cylinder contains two pistons, each with its own seal and seal support. Each piston operates one shoe and they have a common return spring. When the brake is applied both pistons are forced outward and in turn force their shoes to contact the drum.

The handbrake mechanism is operated by cables and levers and is attached to the outer side of the fluid cylinder. It consists of a flat drawlink which has a taper wedge at its inner end. Flat, taper-ended tappets are separated from the wedge by friction-reducing rollers while the outer ends of the tappets contact the moving ends of the shoes. When the handbrake is applied the drawlink is pulled and the taper wedge, operating through the rollers, forces the tappets to move the shoes. The wedge action magnifies the available force, and the operation of the handbrake has no effect upon the fluid part of the assembly.

The shoe pull-off springs are fitted between the shoes in such a way that the edges of the shoes are forced to contact raised platforms on the backplate to maintain their alignment with it.

Hydraulic lever (HL3)

This is similar in principle to that of the Lockheed rear brake previously described. The difference is that the cylinder has only one piston and seal, and no spring. The end of the lever moved by

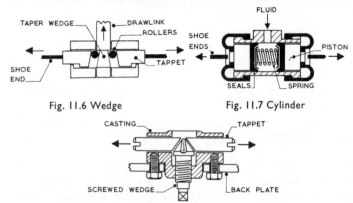

Fig. 11.6 Wedge   Fig. 11.7 Cylinder

Fig. 11.8 Adjuster

the handbrake linkage is engaged in a slot in the cylinder end of the leading shoe. In operation, this end of the shoe contacts the drum and the reaction force moves the cylinder bodily to apply the trailing shoe.

The shoe pull-off springs are fitted between the shoes, and spring-loaded shoe steadies are used. The spring at the adjuster side is coiled for its full length while the other is coiled at each end only.

Adjusters

These may be of the snail-cam type. A snail cam is secured to the backplate near the piston end of each wheel cylinder. The cam has a serrated edge and may be turned from the rear of the backplate by the squared end of its shaft. The leading end of each shoe carries a rigid pin which is forced to contact the cam through the action of the shoe pull-off spring. The turning of the cam forces the shoe nearer the drum, the serrations giving correct clearance and preventing vibration disturbing the adjustment.

TWO-LEADING-SHOE ASSEMBLIES

In these arrangements each shoe has, in effect, its own pivot or anchor and its own expander. Each is forced outwards in the same direction as the normal rotation of the drum. The self-servo action of these shoes is designed to be less than that of a leading shoe used with a trailing shoe, but the use of two leading shoes provides a very powerful and relatively stable brake. Note that the stopping power is very greatly reduced when the direction of rotation of the drum is reversed.

Weight transfer

When the brakes are applied, the normal weight distribution of the vehicle is altered and about 60% of the total weight is applied to the front wheels. As this increases their grip upon the road surface, the more powerful two leading shoe assemblies can be used to obtain greater retardation without the danger of wheel locking and skidding. The possible locking and skidding of the rear wheels, as the weight acting upon them is reduced, may be avoided by the use of leading and trailing shoe assemblies and by the use of a pressure-limiting valve in the rear pipe line.

Lockheed front brake

The shoes are of T-shaped cross-section and are made of steel. Each carries a lining of asbestos material which is riveted or bonded to it. One end of each shoe has a semicircular notch into which is fitted the cam of the 'Micram' adjuster; the other end of each shoe is radiused.

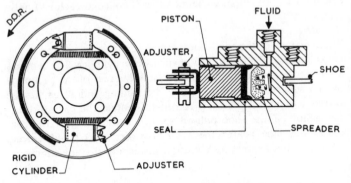

Fig. 11.9 Lockheed front brake   Fig. 11.10 Lockheed cylinder

Between the shoes, and diametrically opposite each other, are shoe-operating cylinders of cast aluminium alloy. These are sealed at one end and are bolted rigidly to the back plate. Each cylinder contains a piston, a rubber cup, a plastic cup spreader, and a small spring. The outer ends of the pistons are slotted and carry the adjuster forks of the adjuster assembly. The radiused ends of the shoes are fitted into flat-bottomed grooves in the sealed end of the cylinders. The shoes are held to the cylinders, and to the backplate, by springs.

The torque reaction forces are transmitted to the stub axle and suspension through the rigidly mounted cylinders and backplate. As the shoes can slide in their slots in the ends of the cylinders and the pistons, they automatically centralize themselves as the brakes are applied. This feature reduces the tendency to 'grab' and tends to even out the wear between the two shoe linings.

The upper or rearmost cylinder is usually connected to the fluid system by a flexible hose of large diameter but small bore. A metal pipe is fitted to connect the two cylinders and the second cylinder, being the farther from the master cylinder, is fitted with a bleed nipple.

Girling front brake

Although there may be slight differences between makes and models of vehicle the basic arrangement is:

One end of each shoe is operated by its own rigidly mounted aluminium-alloy cylinder while the other end is fitted into a steel reinforced slot in the rear face of the opposite cylinder. These slots are so angled that the shoe movement, due to both the piston and the self-servo action, results in *both* ends of the shoe being forced closer to the drum. This feature helps to equalize the braking effect, the rate of wear, and the temperature over the whole area of each lining – so providing a more effective brake.

The shoe pull-off springs are fitted between the rigid backplate (near the cylinder) and the shoe (off-centre towards the slot end).

Steady posts

In order to maintain efficiency and to equalize wear, the shoes and the linings must be kept parallel with the working surface of the drum.

In some spring arrangements the shoes tend to be lifted away from the backplate and this is prevented by the action of small coil or leaf springs. These are fitted under the heads of small pins which pass through the backplate and through holes in the webs of the shoes, the springs forcing their shoe back on to small machined platforms on the backplate.

In other spring arrangements the shoes tend to move too close to the backplate and this is prevented by fixed or adjustable steady posts. These are fitted between the backplate and the shoe web. Where the adjustable type of post is fitted, the alignment of the shoes must be checked whenever they have been disturbed, or when replacement shoes have been fitted.

Cylinders

The cylinders are arranged diametrically opposite each other, and are bolted rigidly to the backplate. They are interconnected by a small metal pipe and the one farthest from the master cylinder is fitted with a bleed nipple. Each cylinder is an aluminium-alloy casting with an accurately machined and polished bore. One end is solid and is reinforced by an angled steel slot which supports the flat end of the opposite shoe. Each cylinder contains a piston, a rubber seal, and a piston-return spring. In some cylinders a die-cast metal seal support may be fitted. A rubber dust-excluding cap is fitted over the ends of the piston and the cylinder and this should be filled by special rubber grease.

LINING MATERIALS

Brake lining materials must have the following properties:
(1) A high coefficient of friction when used with iron or steel.
(2) A coefficient of friction which does not reduce as the temperature is increased.
(3) The ability to resist wear.
(4) Comprehensive and tensile strengths high enough to resist the highest stresses imposed during severe braking.
(5) The ability to be moulded into shape.

Much research is always being carried out to find new lining materials, but the best materials available are still based upon the mineral known as white asbestos. Unfortunately, while this asbestos itself has a high coefficient of friction (about 0·65), when resins and other bonding and strengthening materials are added to obtain other essential properties, the final material has a coefficient of only about 0·3. Modern shoe-lining materials, however, are reasonably suited to their purpose, are fairly long lasting, and are not too expensive, but their coefficient of friction does reduce as their temperature increases. This failing has led to the development of the disc brake with its heat-resistant, smaller, and more expensive pads of special material which do not suffer very much from brake fade.

Types of lining

For many years all brake linings were secured to their shoes by means of brass, copper or aluminium rivets. The disadvantages of riveting are:
(1) The lining may be distorted by the unequal pressures exerted by the rivets.
(2) The countersinking holes reduce the lining area.

(3) Dirt and loose material collect in the countersinking holes and results in the scoring of the drums.

(4) About two-thirds of the lining cannot be used because of the danger of the rivet heads scoring the drum.

(5) Replacing the lining takes considerable time.

These disadvantages are overcome by the more modern method of attaching the linings to the shoes by a bonding process. Bonded shoes have proved to be more firmly attached than riveted shoes and they may be worn much thinner with no danger of scoring the drums. In the bonding process the bonding agent is a thermoplastic resin dissolved in alcohol. This is brushed over the previously buffed surfaces of the steel shoe and the lining, and allowed to stand for about thirty minutes for the alcohol to evaporate. The lining is then correctly positioned on the shoe in a jig, and the assembly heated for about half an hour at a temperature of about 200 °C while the lining and the shoe are forced together under a pressure of about 2800 kN/m². The shoe is then allowed to cool and the lining is buffed to the correct curvature.

DISC BRAKES

Brake fade

Over the years the drum brake has been made very efficient but, as vehicle speeds have increased, the fault known as brake fade has become more important. Brake fade is the loss of retardation, or stopping power, which occurs during application of the brakes. Brake fade is caused by the overheating of the brake assemblies, modern body styles and the use of small-diameter dished wheels making it very difficult to obtain an adequate flow of air over the brake drums. The effect of the excessive heat is to (a) reduce the coefficient of friction between the linings and the drums and (b) cause the drums to expand. In hydraulically operated brakes it may also result in excessive pedal travel. Overheating will usually occur after prolonged use of the brakes, e.g. during very fast driving and when descending very long or steep hills.

Advantages of disc brakes

All disc brakes are based on the principle of a wheel-driven disc being retarded by pressure-operated friction pads. These pads are carried in a caliper which straddles the disc and which is mounted upon a torque arm secured to the suspension. Disc brakes have the following advantages over drum brakes:

(1) Greater heat dissipation. This is because only a small part of the disc is heated by contact with the pads, the greater part always being in contact with the stream of cooling air. Brake fade is therefore greatly reduced, and pedal travel remains fairly constant.

(2) Cleaner braking surfaces. Centrifugal force throws water, dirt, and oil off the discs, which therefore retain their efficiency and are worn less. The discs are more substantial and so less liable to distortion than drums.

(3) Lighter in weight. The disc-brake assembly is about 20% less in weight than the equivalent drum type.

(4) Simpler construction. Pads are visible and wear is easy to see.

(5) Easier service. Pads can be changed much quicker than shoes.

Disadvantages

(1) The disc brake has no self servo action, so higher operating forces and pressures are required. In spite of this feature the disc brake, particularly when used with a hydraulic servo unit, provides a braking effort which is directly proportional to the applied pedal force.

(2) The higher operating forces required complicate the design of the hand-brake mechanism. For this reason many cars are fitted with disc brakes at the front wheels only.

Girling disc brake

Construction

The disc is made of cast iron and is bolted to the wheel hub, so that its flat surfaces are vertical. An inverted, U-shaped caliper of cast iron is fitted over the disc and is bolted to the stub axle assembly. This assembly therefore acts as a torque arm which resists the reaction forces from the braking torque. Each side of the caliper contains a fluid cylinder and a piston, a rubber piston sealing ring set in a recess in the cylinder wall, a dust cover, and a pad assembly. The cylinders are interconnected by a bridge pipe or by a drilled hole, the one nearest the master cylinder being connected to the system by a flexible hose. The cylinder farthest from the master cylinder is fitted with a bleed nipple.

Each pad assembly consists of a steel backplate to which is bonded a segment-shaped pad of special friction material. The

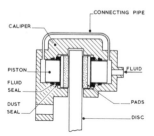

Fig. 11.11 Girling disc brake

pads are located and retained in the caliper by bolted-on retainer plates, or lock pins.

Operation

When the brakes are applied, and little or no wear has taken place, the slight piston movement necessary is obtained without relative movement between the piston and its seal, i.e. the piston movement distorts the seal. When the brakes are released the seal regains its shape and retracts the piston – maintaining a light rubbing contact between the pads and the disc. This contact is due to the combination of the friction between the seal and the piston, and the static head of brake fluid, i.e. this is a 'hydro-static' brake.

When wear has occurred the piston moves slightly through its seal to take up a new position in the cylinder, i.e. it automatically compensates for the wear, and the hydrostatic effect automatically ensures the correct light rubbing contact when the brakes are released.

Service

System. The fluid system requires the normal service procedure.
Pad wear. Pad wear may be checked by direct inspection, stripping of the assembly not being necessary. Pads should be replaced when worn down to about 3 mm thickness. After removing the retainer

plates or pins, the pads can be pulled out by hand. The pistons must then be forced back into their cylinders simultaneously, the new pads inserted, and the retainer plates refitted. When all the new pads are fitted, the pistons must be forced to take up their new positions in their cylinders by operating the foot pedal a few times.
Disc wear. After a very long period of service the discs may be found to be badly scored, distorted, or to suffer from surface cracking. Faulty discs should always be replaced by new units.

Some calipers are made in two parts and are bolted together. They must never be split during normal service but this may have to be done (to replace the piston seals) during a complete overhaul. Disc brakes usually have the same life as an engine, e.g. about 80 000 km.

Master cylinders
The master cylinder is used to convert the applied pedal force into pressure in a fluid system. The Lockheed master cylinders increase an existing pressure (residual or standing pressure) and the Girling master cylinders permit the free passage of fluid to and from the system until the cylinder is operated. Their first action then is to enclose the fluid by closing off a port.

GIRLING MASTER CYLINDERS

There are two main types:
(1) The centre valve (CV) type.
(2) The compression barrel (CB) type.

Both operate on the same principal, and in both the fluid can flow freely between cylinder and system when the brakes are off.

Centre valve (CV) master cylinder
This type is intended for use with the suspended type of pedal. The reservoir may be separate, or integral with the cylinder.

Construction and operation
The cylinder is an aluminium-alloy casting, the bore of which is very accurately machined to size and then polished to provide a fine surface finish. A drilled hole or port connects the end of the bore with the fluid reservoir and another drilled hole, in the upper

part of the cylinder, allows fluid to pass between the reservoir and the system.

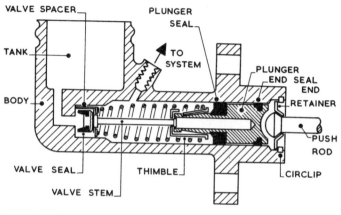

Fig. 11.12 Girling centre-valve master cylinder

The cylinder contains a valve stem and centre valve assembly, a spring and a spring thimble, and a plunger with main and end seals of rubber. The outer end of the plunger is concave and is contacted by a ball-ended push rod operated by the brake pedal.

Brakes applied. When the pedal is depressed the push rod takes up its clearance and then contacts the outer end of the plunger. The first 0·8 mm of plunger movement forces the centre valve to close the end port to the reservoir – so enclosing the fluid in the cylinder and in the system. Continued plunger movement reduces the effective volume and so increases the pressure. The increased pressure acts equally throughout the system and the wheel cylinder pistons are forced outward to apply the shoes to the drums. Further plunger movement maintains or increases pressure until pedal is released.

Brakes released. When the pedal is released the plunger return spring, assisted by the fluid pressure due to the action of the shoe pull-off springs, forces the plunger back down the cylinder. As it reaches the end of its stroke, the centre valve is drawn away from the end port, and the fluid passes from the system back into the reservoir. This recuperating, or recharging, action automatically compensates for fluid expansion and small fluid losses, and ensures that the cylinder is ready for use again.

Compression barrel (CB) master cylinder
Construction and operation
These types have a separate reservoir. The plunger is in the form of a hollow cylinder which encloses its return spring. One end of the plunger is solid and is shaped to fit the end of the push rod. This end is fitted with a rubber sealing ring. The open end of the plunger passes through a metal shim and a rubber recuperating and sealing ring. The ring is located in a recess in the end of the cylinder and is enclosed by a metal support. When the brakes are off, four small holes, drilled in the side of the plunger just behind the sealing ring, permit the free flow of fluid between the system and the reservoir.

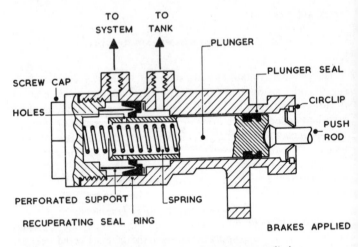

Fig. 11.13 Girling compression-barrel master cylinder

Brakes applied. When the pedal is depressed the plunger is forced inwards against the action of its spring. The first 1·5 mm of its movement causes the four drilled holes to pass through the seal, so sealing off the reservoir and enclosing the fluid in the master cylinder and system. Continued pedal movement builds up the pressure which then operates the wheel cylinder pistons.

Brakes released. When the pedal is released the plunger is forced outwards by its spring. The last 1·5 mm of its movement allows the four holes to move back clear of the seal and, in effect, to reconnect the reservoir to the system. The pressure at once collapses and the fluid is returned to the reservoir by the action of the shoe pull-off springs on the wheel cylinder pistons.

LOCKHEED MASTER CYLINDER

Construction and operation

The unit consists of a cast aluminium-alloy cylinder with external mounting lugs, this type being used with the suspended type of

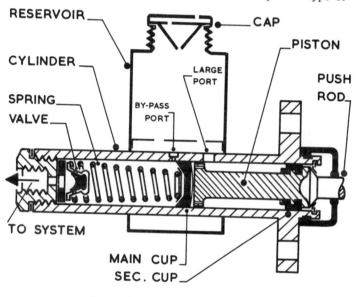

Fig. 11.14 Lockheed master cylinder

pedal. The cylinder passes through a tank or reservoir fitted with a screw cap so designed that while air can enter dirt cannot. The cylinder contains a double-acting check valve and seat, a spring, main and secondary rubber cups, and an aluminium-alloy piston.

The forward end of the piston is flat and is perforated by a ring of small holes. The main rubber sealing cup is fitted in front of the piston face, and the rubber of the cup is prevented from entering the holes by a flexible metal disc. The rear end of the piston is sealed into the bore by the secondary rubber cup. This end of the piston has a hemispherical recess into which is fitted the end of the push rod of the brake pedal. The push rod and the piston are retained in the cylinder by a domed washer and a circlip. The end of the cylinder is enclosed by a rubber boot to exclude dirt and moisture.

A relatively large spring is fitted between the main cup and the check valve, the cup being protected by a cupped washer which fits into or over the end of the spring. The spring is used to return the piston and to load the check valve. The valve assembly consists of a metal dome with a flange which seats on a rubber seal ring in the end of the cylinder. The dome is pierced by a number of small holes which are normally blanked off by a rubber cup secured to the inner side of the dome. Different types of check valve are in service but the principle of operation is the same.

Two ports are arranged between the cylinder and the reservoir. The large port connects with the space behind the piston head while the small, or by-pass, port connects with the space in front of the main cup – while the brakes are off. Both spaces, i.e. the cylinder, must be filled with brake fluid at all times.

The master cylinders used for both brakes and clutches are very similar, the difference being that the clutch types do not usually have a check valve. This is because the standing pressure would cause extra wear to the clutch-release bearing, and might also cause clutch slip. The clutch master cylinder can be identified by a groove machined around the outlet end of the cylinder. Where a twin-bore master cylinder is fitted, the clutch cylinder has a grooved end plug, is labelled, or is marked by etching.

Brakes applied. When the brake pedal is depressed the push rod forces the piston along the cylinder, pushing the main cup in front of it and compressing the spring. When the main cup shuts off the by-pass port the fluid is completely enclosed and continued piston movement builds up the pressure in the forward end of the cylinder. When this pressure exceeds that of the standing pressure (about 55 kN/m²) in the pipe lines and wheel cylinders, the *difference* between the two pressures forces the rubber cup in the check valve away from the metal dome. The higher pressure is at once transmitted, through the small holes in the dome, to all parts of the system equally. The wheel cylinder pistons are forced outwards to apply their shoes to the drums, and so retard the motion of the vehicle. Continued pedal and piston movement maintains or increases the forces holding the shoes in contact with the drums.

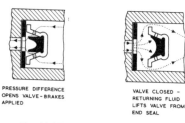

PRESSURE DIFFERENCE
OPENS VALVE - BRAKES
APPLIED

VALVE CLOSED –
RETURNING FLUID
LIFTS VALVE FROM
END SEAL

Fig. 11.15 Check valve operation

Brakes released. The fluid behind the piston head is used to refill, or recuperate, the forward part of the cylinder each time the brakes are released. It also, by keeping the bore wet with fluid, reduces wear on the main cup and helps to provide better sealing against the entry of air into the system. When the pedal is released the push rod is withdrawn and the piston spring forces the piston back down the cylinder very quickly. The sudden piston movement results in a sudden pressure drop in the forward part of the cylinder, and the pressure difference forces fluid to flow through the holes in the piston head to refill this space. This action also reduces back pressure on the piston and so helps to provide a quicker release of the brakes. The rear portion of the cylinder is at once refilled from the reservoir, via the large port. The fluid in the wheel cylinders and pipe lines is now at a higher pressure than that in the cylinder, and the shoe pull-off springs are retracting their pistons. As the holes in the body or dome of the check valve are sealed off by the rubber cup the returning fluid lifts the whole valve assembly away from the end seat, compressing the spring. The returning fluid displaces the fluid already in the forward part of the cylinder, forcing it to return to the reservoir via the by-pass port. (This is the spray which can be seen during bleeding operations.)

The action of the returning fluid continues until the pipe line pressure is equalled by the spring loading of the check valve. The valve is then returned to its seat and the system is sealed off from the master cylinder. The recuperating action occurs each time the brakes are released and ensures that:

(a) The standing pressure is maintained.

(b) Any fluid expansion due to heating is compensated for.

(c) Any small fluid losses are made up.

In this way the master cylinder is kept fully charged and ready for use.

BRAKING EFFICIENCY

Vehicle braking efficiency is the ratio between the retardation, or deceleration, of the vehicle and the acceleration due to gravity, or *g*, expressed as a percentage.

Retardation and *g* are both measured in units of metre second per second and braking efficiency may be calculated from the formula:

$$\text{braking efficiency} = \frac{\text{retardation } (\text{m/s}^2) \times 100}{g \; (=9\cdot81 \text{ m/s}^2)}$$

If the retardation were equal to *g* the braking efficiency would be 100% – a value seldom found in practice.

Brake testing

In practice, braking efficiencies may be determined by:

(a) Measuring the stopping distance for a given speed.

(b) Using a decelerometer such as the Tapley or Ferodo meters.

(c) Using a brake-testing machine.

Stopping distance

In the first method the vehicle is driven at a steady speed on a level road. The brakes are applied and the distance covered between applying the brakes and stopping the vehicle is measured. The test should be repeated in opposite directions, and at the same speed, to reduce possible inaccuracies resulting from the effects of wind and slight variations in road gradient. Tyre pressures must of course be correct. When the stopping distance for a given speed is known, the braking efficiency may be determined from tables such as those published by the brake manufacturers and the motoring organizations. These tables are based on the above formula and they may also give some idea of braking quality in relation to efficiency.

Example. From a speed of 48 km/h a vehicle is brought to rest through a distance of 18 m. From the table this indicates a braking efficiency of 50%. Similarly, if the speed had been 38 km/h and the stopping distance 12 m the braking efficiency would have been 50%.

Stopping distance in metres from 40 km/h	from 48 km/h	Efficiency %	Quality
21	30	30	very poor (dangerous)
16	23	40	poor
12	18	50	fair
11	15	60	good
9	13	70	very good
8	11	80	excellent

Decelerometer

In the second method the brake efficiency is indicated directly by the meter. The Tapley meter records the effect of the retardation upon a pendulum, i.e. it records how far a pendulum is forced from the vertical. The more powerful the retardation the greater the swing of the pendulum, and vice versa. The pendulum swing is hydraulically damped to enable the instrument to be used in a vehicle subjected to vibration and road shocks, and it must be carefully zeroed while the vehicle is on level ground, i.e. the pendulum must be vertical before the test is carried out. The motion of the pendulum is copied by a magnet pivoting about the same point, the magnet rotating a circular scale by the action of a gear and quadrant.

The Ferodo meter is similar in principal, but a steel ball is fitted inside a curved tube. The tube tilts under the influence of the retardation force, and this results in shutters of different colours becoming visible through small windows. The shutters indicate the percentage of braking efficiency and the stopping distance from 32 km/h at that efficiency. Once again the tilting motion of the tube is damped, and the meter must be carefully zeroed at the beginning of the test.

Other instruments are available in which the pendulum carries a pen or stylus at its lower end. As the pendulum swings, the stylus traces a line on a curved paper scale, the length of the line indicating the percentage braking efficiency. The line will also indicate any tendency of the brakes to pull to one side.

In all of these instruments the indicators remain fixed until they are manually cancelled, so that the driver does not have to watch the instrument while driving and braking.

Test machines

Tests of braking efficiency may also be carried out by means of much larger, more elaborate, and more expensive machines. As might reasonably be expected, these machines can test not only the overall efficiency but the retardation torque exerted by each brake and wheel assembly. It is possible therefore to check, and correct, unequal braking efforts between the near- and off-side assemblies, and the proportioning of the braking effort between the front and rear wheels. There are two main types of machine available, the platform and the roller type.

In the platform type, the vehicle is driven on to four platforms, at a speed of between 6 km and 13 km/h, and the brakes applied. As the brakes operate, the wheels move the platforms against a fixed resistance, the extent of the movement of the individual platforms being indicated upon dial gauges or columns of liquid. The four indicators are calibrated in hundreds of newtons and are automatically cancelled as the vehicle is driven off the platforms.

In the roller type, the rollers are of steel and have a diamond tread pattern. They are arranged in pairs at each side of the machine, and each pair is driven by an electric motor in such a way that their torque reaction can be measured. The reactions are transmitted to gauges by a hydraulic system and the gauges are calibrated in hundreds of newtons. These machines test front and rear wheel brakes separately. The motors are set running and the gauges are zeroed. The vehicle is driven on to the machine in such a way that the front wheels contact the rollers and the brakes are then applied. The resistance the wheels offer to the rotation of the rollers results in a torque reaction which is indicated on the dials. The two gauge readings are recorded and the gauges zeroed again ready for the rear brake test, the vehicle being driven forward to bring the rear wheels on to the rollers. The hand brake may also be checked.

The total retardation force is the sum of the separate braking forces in hundreds of newtons. The braking efficiency may then be calculated from the formula, or determined from the manufacturers charts. The vehicle weight must be known. The presence of oil on the linings, or of oval brake drums will be indicated by fluctuating movements of the gauge.

BRAKING SYSTEM FAULTS

Some of the more common faults and their causes are given in Table 11.1.

Table 11.1 Braking system: faults, causes and remedies

Faults	Causes	Remedies
1. Brakes not operating	(a) Shortage of fluid in master cylinder	Top up to correct level with correct make and grade of fluid
	(b) Main cup leaking pressure	Replace master cylinder or rebuild with new rubber parts. Bleed the system
	(c) Pipe broken in system	Fit new pipe, and bleed the system
2. Inefficient brakes (lack of stopping power)	(a) Oil or grease on linings	If fresh, clean off with petrol. If soaked into linings, fit new linings
	(b) Incorrect lining material	Fit new linings of correct make and type
	(c) Linings not bedded to drums	Give some hard usage when road conditions are safe to do so
	(d) Tyres worn smooth	Fit replacement tyres of the recommended make and pattern. Keep to the recommended pressures
	(e) Vehicle overloaded	Work within the proper weight limits of the vehicle at all times
3. Grabbing brakes	(a) Shoes need adjusting	Adjust to correct shoe-to-drum clearance
	(b) Shoes not centralizing	Clean and lubricate shoe ends and slots, and sliding cylinders
	(c) Shoes seized on pivots	Clean and lubricate
	(d) New linings	Give hard usage to bed shoes to drums. Remove sharp leading edge of lining
	(e) Scored or distorted drums	Fit new drums, or have liners fitted
	(f) Loose spring or suspension bolts	Tighten or renew bolts or rubber bushes
4. Dragging brakes	(a) Handbrake linkage seized	Clean, release, and lubricate
	(b) Pedal spring broken	Fit new spring
	(c) Insufficient pedal clearance	Adjust to correct clearance (about 25 mm at pedal pad)
	(d) By-pass port blocked (Lockheed)	Strip and clean master cylinder. Bleed system
	(e) Shoes over-adjusted	Adjust to correct clearance. Ease and lubricate

239

Fault	Cause	Remedy
	(f) Sliding cylinder seized	Clean and lubricate cylinder faces and back-plate
	(g) Weak pull-off shoe springs	Fit new springs of the correct pattern
	(h) Cups swollen due to contamination by mineral oil	Replace all rubber parts in system. See note on contamination
5. Pulling to one side	(a) Incorrect tyre pressures	Inflate to correct pressures all round. Check tread for same degree of wear at each side
	(b) Oil on linings at opposite side	Clean off completely, or fit new linings
	(c) Distorted or cracked drum	Replace by new drum
	(d) Different lining materials	Fit new linings of correct make and type
	(e) Choked flexible pipe one side	Fit new pipe and bleed system
	(f) Excessively worn steering and suspension joints	Adjust or replace as required
	(g) Loose backplate bolts	Tighten or renew if chattered
	(h) Spring centre bolt broken	Fit new bolt – examine spring for further damage. Replace if in poor condition
	(i) Chassis broken	Restore alignment, and repair chassis
6. Excessive pedal travel	(a) Master cylinder level too low	Top up to correct level with correct make and grade of fluid
	(b) Pedal push rod needs adjusting	Adjust to give correct pedal pad clearance
	(c) Master cylinder bolts slack	Tighten
	(d) Master cylinder main cup not sealing properly	Fit new rubber parts or new cylinder. Bleed system
	(e) Pipes or connections leaking	Tighten or replace and bleed system
	(f) Shoes need adjusting or relining	Adjust, or fit new shoes and linings and adjust
7. Spongy pedal / Springy pedal	(a) Air in system	Bleed system
	(b) Master cylinder cup not sealing	Fit new master cylinder or service old unit
		Bleed system
	(c) Linings not bedded to drums	Give hard usage when and where safe to do so
	(d) Linings mixed during repairs	As above
	(e) Drums weakened by skimming	Fit new drums or fit liners to old drums
	(f) Master cylinder bolts slack	Tighten

Bleeding the system

Bleeding is the name given to the operation by which air is expelled from the system. It is not a routine service operation and should only be necessary when (a) the level in the master cylinder has been allowed to fall too low, (b) the fluid has been drained off or (c) the system has been opened for repair. In Girling systems air may be drawn in through the wheel cylinders if the seals have become excessively worn.

Air, unlike the fluid, can be compressed, and its presence in the system makes the brakes less effective and very unreliable.

As there are important differences between the bleeding operation of the Lockheed and the Girling systems both are dealt with.

Lockheed

(1) Adjust all the brakes to provide the correct shoe-to-drum clearances.

(2) Top up the fluid reservoir with the correct make and type of fluid. Keep topping up at intervals to prevent the possible entry of air while bleeding.

(3) Fit a rubber pipe to bleeding nipple of one *rear* brake. Immerse the other end of the pipe in a small quantity of fluid in a clean glass jar, keeping the end of the pipe below the surface.

(4) Slacken off the nipple by one complete turn. Depress the brake pedal and then allow it to return freely.

(5) Repeat the operation, with a slight pause between the pedal strokes, until air bubbles can no longer be seen in the jar.

(6) Hold down the pedal and tighten the bleeding nipple.

(7) Repeat the operation at the other rear wheel, and then at the front wheels.

(8) Top up and clean the reservoir and its surroundings with methylated spirits. Check the cap for clear vent holes.

Girling

(1) Ensure that the brake pedal is free from obstruction.

(2) Slacken back the adjusters (anticlockwise) on the front drum brakes.

(3) Lock up the rear adjusters (clockwise).

(4) If drum or disc brakes are fitted all round, start bleeding at the near-side rear wheel.

(5) If disc front and drum rear brakes are fitted, start bleeding at the front near-side wheel.

(6) Connect the rubber bleeding pipe to the nipple with the other end of the pipe below the surface of a small quantity of clean fluid in a clean glass jar. Slacken the nipple by one half-turn.

(7) Where a centre-valve (aluminium alloy) master cylinder is fitted, give the pedal one full stroke. Follow this by three short and quick strokes and then allow the pedal to return freely. Repeat this sequence until no more air bubbles can be seen in the jar. Replenish the master cylinder and keep checking the level and topping-up as the operation continues. Lock up the nipple when air ceases to show in the jar.

(8) Where the compression-barrel (cast iron) master cylinder is fitted, give slow, full-length, pedal strokes and allow the pedal to return freely. Wait three or four seconds between strokes and continue bleeding until no more air bubbles are seen.

(9) Repeat the bleeding operation at the other side wheel, and then at the remaining wheels.

(10) Reset all the shoe adjusters to provide their proper clearances.

12 The Ignition and Starter Systems

System

Function. The function of the coil ignition system is to provide, at the correct time and in the correct sequence, a series of sparks of sufficient intensity to ignite the highly compressed mixture of air and petrol in the cylinders of the engine.

Units. The complete system consists of:

(1) A battery which supplies voltage (6 volts or 12 volts) to force a small current through the primary winding of the ignition coil.

(2) A contact breaker, or engine-operated switch, which interrupts the flow of battery current through the primary winding of the coil at regular and predetermined intervals.

(3) An ignition coil or transformer which converts the battery voltage into a voltage high enough to cause a spark to jump the gap between the points of a spark plug in a highly compressed mixture of air and fuel.

(4) A condenser which helps to provide a stronger spark and also reduces the arcing or burning of the points of the contact breaker.

(5) A distributor which directs the high voltage current to the spark plug of whichever cylinder is nearing top dead centre on its compression stroke.

(6) A spark plug for each engine cylinder. This introduces the spark into the compressed mixture of air and fuel in the cylinder.

An ignition switch is used to control the flow of battery current through the contact breaker and the primary winding of the ignition coil. An ignition warning lamp is fitted inside the vehicle to indicate when current is flowing through the circuit – and when the charging circuit is not charging the battery.

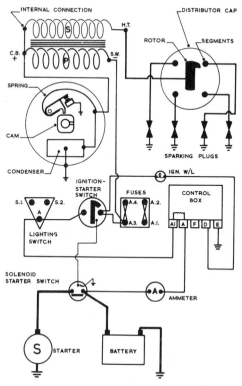

Fig. 12.1 Ignition circuit

Ignition coil

Construction

The coil is a form of transformer, and consists of two windings over the same core. The core is made from soft-iron rods or plates, soft iron being used because it is easy to magnetize and de-magnetize and because it does not retain magnetism. Separate rods or plates are used to reduce the heating effect of the magnetic fields and the primary current.

The secondary winding is wound over the core but is insulated from it. This winding consists of many hundreds of turns of very thin, varnish insulated, copper wire. One end of the secondary

winding is connected to the high voltage (HT) terminal of the coil
terminal block and the other end is connected to the terminal
marked positive or CB (contact breaker) in coils used in positive
earth systems.

The primary winding is wound over, but insulated from, the

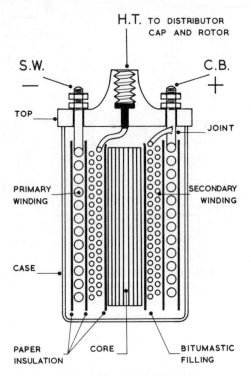

Fig. 12.2 Ignition coil

secondary winding and consists of a few hundred turns of relatively
thick insulated copper wire. One end of this winding is connected
to the CB or positive terminal while the other end is connected to
the negative or SW (switch) terminal.

The usual turn ratio of the two windings is about fifty turns of
secondary winding to each turn of primary winding. The complete

core and winding assembly is sealed into a metal case by a bitu-mastic material.

NOTE. The battery connection to the chassis may be from either the positive or the negative terminal post of the battery. Present-day systems mostly use the negative earth connection. Coils marked CB and SW are made for either positive or negative earth systems and are usually marked to indicate which – being wound to suit the system used. Coils marked + and – will operate correctly in either system provided they are connected into the circuit in the correct way.

Operation

When the battery current is passed through the primary winding to earth it produces a magnetic field which passes through both windings and which is concentrated by the soft-iron core. The *motion* of the field across the coils *induces* a short-lived current in *both* windings.

When the battery current is stopped by the opening of the con-tact breaker points, the magnetic field collapses. This motion of the field across the windings again induces a current in *each* wind-ing, but this time the currents are much greater because the motion of the field across the windings is much faster, i.e. the field collapses faster than it can be established. The current produced in the secondary winding by the collapse of the field is therefore the one used to supply the spark plugs – the other being allowed to pass to earth. Note that the induced currents are very short-lived, lasting only as long as there is relative movement between the magnetic field and the windings.

The current induced in the secondary winding has about fifty times the voltage of that induced in the primary winding, due to the turn ratio, and in this way the low voltage of the battery is transformed into the high voltage (about 16 000 volts) required to cause a spark to jump in the highly compressed air-fuel mixture. The higher the compression of the engine the higher the voltage required to force the spark across the plug points.

The lower voltage induced in the *primary* winding at the same moment always *opposes* the collapse of the magnetic field, and the stopping of the battery current flow which causes it, and tries to keep the current flowing across the points of the contact breaker as they are opened. This self-induced current, by slowing the collapse of the magnetic field, reduces the voltage available at the plug points and so causes a less intense spark. A condenser is therefore fitted, in parallel with the points of the contact breaker, which holds this self-induced current while the points are being opened, and discharges it while they are being closed. By making possible a cleaner break in the flow of the primary current when the points open, and by increasing the strength of the current when the points are closed, the condenser plays a very important part in the obtaining of a very intense (strong) spark. It also increases the life of the contact points by reducing the burning of the points (arcing).

Negative spark
Ignition coils are usually wound in such a way that the insulated centre electrode of the spark plug is negative in relation to the

Fig. 12.3 Erosion of spark plug. Excessive wear (dishing) on earth electrode, with comparatively little wear on centre electrode – indicates wrong polarity, which reduces ignition efficiency

engine or earth. The spark travels by ionizing the mixture between the plug points and, because electrons flow more readily from a hot surface to a colder one, the spark can be obtained under a lower voltage when the centre electrode is negative than when it is positive.

The advantages of the negative spark are that about 10% less voltage is required, there is less electrical stress in the high-voltage circuit, and erosion of the distributor rotor and the segments is reduced. A further advantage is that, as the centre electrodes of the spark plugs are eroded, the earth electrodes can be carefully bent to restore the gap to its correct size. Erosion in a spark plug occurs mainly at the centre electrode and only to a slight extent at the earth electrode. If the reverse is found, it indicates that the coil is connected the wrong way round.

Insulated return coil
The coils used in insulated return systems are slightly different from that just described. In these the end of the secondary winding inside the coil is connected to the coil case instead of to the primary winding at the CB terminal. The coil case must be earthed to complete the circuit. In some of these coils a fourth terminal is fitted to which is connected the secondary winding and an earth connecting wire.

Oil coil
In order to provide an adequate and reliable ignition spark for high-speed, high-compression engines, the secondary circuit voltage must be increased from the usual 10000 to 16000 volts to between 25000 to 30000 volts. The increased coil output results in increased heating of the windings, and in these coils this very undesirable heat is dissipated by immersing the winding assembly in a low-viscosity vegetable oil held in a plastic container. The container is not filled but it is sealed. These coils should be mounted vertically and should preferably be in a cooling air stream.

Oil coils provide better cold starting, and reduce the tendency to misfire when some of the weaker air-fuel mixtures have to be ignited.

The condenser
Construction
The condenser consists of a series of tinfoil plates insulated from each other by waxed paper. In many modern units, strips of these materials are used and are wound into a cylinder. The cylinder is then sealed into a small case mounted near, and in parallel with, the points of the contact breaker in the distributor unit. One set

of plates is earthed through the case while the other set is connected to the contact point connected to the CB terminal of the coil.

Operation

When the points of the contact breaker are closed, a current of battery voltage flows through the primary winding of the coil to earth, inducing a much higher voltage current in each winding. These two currents are passed to earth via the points of the contact breaker.

When the points are opened and the battery voltage current flow is suddenly stopped, high voltage currents are again induced in each winding. The very high voltage current induced in the secondary winding now passes to earth through the points of the spark plug of whichever cylinder is near top dead centre on its compression stroke. At the same instant the current induced in the primary winding (at about 300 volts) tries to pass between the opening points – but is instead directed into the condenser. The condenser cannot pass this current but it can contain or hold it, i.e. it becomes charged.

When the contact breaker points meet again this current is discharged from the condenser in the same direction as the flow of the battery current – increasing the voltage through the primary winding, increasing the strength of the magnetic field, and increasing the voltage available at the spark plug points.

Contact breaker

Construction

The contact breaker consists of two tungsten-tipped contact points arranged in the upper part of the distributor body. One contact is earthed through the body, and its position on the base plate can be adjusted and locked by a clamp screw. The other contact is mounted upon an insulating fibre block which has a heel always in contact with a cam. The block is riveted to a strip of spring steel which is insulated from the other contact and the distributor body. The insulated contact is moved away from the fixed, earth contact by the action of an engine-driven cam, contact being maintained by the flat spring. The cam is driven from the engine camshaft at half the speed of the crankshaft, and usually has the same number of lobes as the engine has cylinders. The cam makes and breaks the primary circuit of the ignition coil, the insulated contact being connected to the CB or positive terminal of the coil.

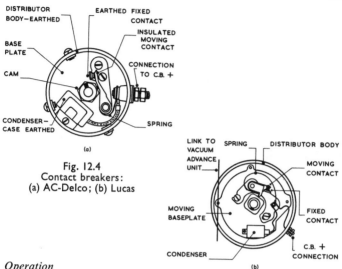

Fig. 12.4
Contact breakers:
(a) AC-Delco; (b) Lucas

Operation

Whatever the design of the engine, the contact breaker must interrupt the flow of current through the primary winding of the coil, at the correct moment in relation to the positions of the pistons in their cylinders. The contacts are usually timed to the engine in such a way that they are just breaking the circuit as number one piston reaches top dead centre on its compression stroke, with the ignition advance set at full retard. As it takes a certain time to fully establish the magnetic field in the coil, the gap between the points of the contact breaker must be set and maintained at the correct size. In the older units this gap was 0·3 mm but in the modern units it is between 0·35 mm and 0·40 mm.

Incorrect contact breaker gaps

Too large a gap will (a) advance timing of the spark, (b) weaken spark, and (c) cause misfiring and pinking.

Too small a gap will: (a) retard timing of spark, (b) overload condenser and cause point burning, and (c) cause misfiring and loss of power.

Dwell angle

The dwell angle of the contact breaker cam is of very great importance to high-speed engine performance. Dwell angle is the angle through which the cam turns while the points remain *closed*. The size of the angle depends upon the angle between the cam lobes, and the gap between the points. It must be sufficiently large to enable the core of the ignition coil to become magnetically saturated, i.e. to build up the magnetic field to its maximum strength and so enable the coil to provide the maximum strength of spark.

Too small a dwell angle will result in smaller spark voltages and weaker sparks. This may be caused by:

(a) The contact breaker gap being too large.

(b) The cam being excessively worn.

(c) The cam and shaft bearings being excessively worn.

Too large a dwell angle will result in over-saturation of the coil windings at low speeds. This will in turn lead to overloading of the condenser and the burning of the points of the contact breaker. Too large a dwell angle is usually due to the gap of the contact breaker being too small.

The correct dwell angles are given in test information sheets and are always less than the angle between the cam lobes, e.g. in a six-cylinder distributor unit the lobe angle will be 60°, but the dwell angle will be about 36°.

Multiple contact breakers

Where more than four cylinders are involved, the increased number of lobes necessary on a single cam may lead to ignition troubles, especially in high-speed engines. These arise from a reduced dwell angle, and the effects of inertia and spring lag. To avoid these difficulties six- and eight-cylinder engines are often fitted with twin contact breakers, i.e. a three-lobed cam operates two contact breakers in a six-cylinder distributor, and a four-lobed cam operates two contact breakers in an eight cylinder.

It is important that the rocker arms of the contact breaker be correctly synchronized, or half of the engine spark timing may be earlier or later than the other half. The adjustment for this is usually set and locked by the manufacturer and should never be disturbed when adjusting the points gap. Special synchronizing gauges, and instruction for their use, are available for these special types.

Many American engines have a different type of twin contact breaker. In these the cam has the normal number of lobes, i.e. six or eight, but the contact breakers are connected in parallel between the primary winding and earth. The cam rotates at half engine speed and the first contacts open while the second contacts are closed. This has the effect of doubling the period for which the points are normally closed (hence doubling the dwell angle), and results in a stronger spark. As the contact breakers are in parallel, no spark occurs until the second contact points open.

Advance and retard

Once the spark has ignited the compressed mixture of air and petrol, there is a small delay before the burning mixture expands fully and reaches its maximum pressure. This must be timed to occur when the piston has just passed over top dead centre and is in the best position to exert the maximum force upon the crankpin.

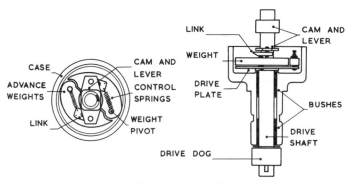

Fig. 12.5 Drive mechanisms

The speed at which the flame spreads through the mixture is constant, for a given mixture strength, but the speed of the piston varies with the speed of the engine. To make these two factors co-incide at all engine speeds it is necessary to make the points of the contact breaker open earlier as the engine speed is increased, and later as the engine speed is reduced. This is carried out automatically by the advance and retard mechanisms.

Mechanical advance

The contact-breaker cam is formed upon a small shaft which is co-axial with the drive shaft, and which is linked to it by small levers fitted into spring-loaded advance weights. These weights are mounted on a circular drive plate secured to the drive shaft in such a way that centrifugal force, as the plate is rotated, forces the weights to move outwards from the centre. As this occurs, the cam is turned relative to the drive shaft and so alters the timing of the

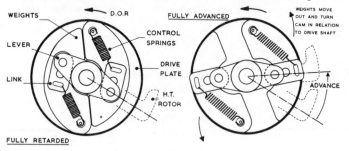

Fig. 12.6 Mechanical advance

spark, advancing it as the piston and engine speed increases. Small control springs are used to return the weights to the centre, and to offer a pre-calculated resistance to their outward motion. In some units, one spring may appear slack. This is normal, and permits a faster advance at certain speed ranges. The mechanical advance assembly is a centrifugal control which makes the ignition timing sensitive to engine *speed*.

Vacuum advance

Another device is incorporated which makes the ignition timing sensitive to the loading on the engine. This is the vacuum advance-and-retard unit which moves the base of the contact breaker to suit the degree of depression in the inlet manifold. This retards the ignition timing when the manifold depression is high (throttle almost closed) and also when the throttle is open but the piston speed is low (engine working against an excessive load).

The base plate of the distributor unit is pivoted, and is linked to a diaphragm fitted inside a sealed chamber. One side of the chamber is subjected to atmospheric pressure while the opposite side is subjected to manifold depression. The difference between the two pressures causes the diaphragm to move and so moves the base

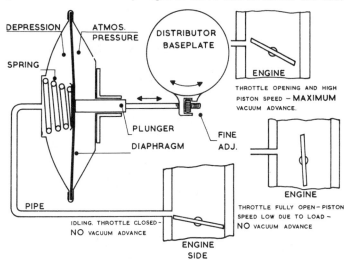

Fig. 12.7 Vacuum advance

plate. A spring is fitted inside the chamber to return the diaphragm and the plate to their zero position.

The distributor

Function

This is the unit in the ignition system which directs the high-voltage current, produced in the secondary winding of the coil, to the spark plugs in the correct firing order.

Construction

The distributor consists of an insulated rotor arm which is mounted above, and rotated by, the camshaft of the contact breaker. Fitted over the rotor arm is an insulated cap containing brass or aluminium segments which are connected to the spark plugs by high-voltage insulated cables. There is an air gap between these segments and the end of the rotor arm. The centre of the arm is connected to the high-voltage terminal of the ignition coil by a high-voltage insulated cable and a small, spring-loaded, carbon brush or pad.

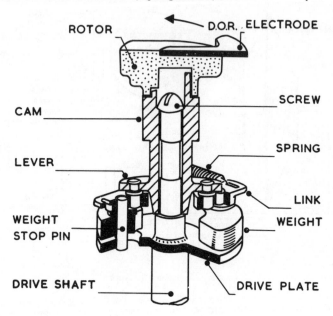

Fig. 12.8 Advance mechanism

The spark plug

Function

To introduce a high-voltage and intense electric spark into the highly compressed and heated charge of mixture in the combustion chamber of the engine cylinder.

Conditions

The spark plug must operate efficiently under pressures varying from $620 \, kN/m^2$ to about $4120 \, kN/m^2$, and temperatures of between $400 \, °C$ and $900 \, °C$. It must remain gas-tight under these conditions and deliver up to 40 intense sparks per second. The plug must also be designed to operate at a temperature high enough to prevent the formation of carbon deposits (over $300 \, °C$) but not so high that it can ignite the mixture before the timed spark (800 °C – 900 °C). This is called the heat range of the plug.

Heat range

Plugs which have a higher heat range are called hot plugs, and vice versa. Hot plugs have a long insulator tip at the firing end, so that the escaping heat has to traverse a long path before passing into the metal of the cylinder head; more heat is therefore retained by the plug. Cold plugs have a shorter insulator tip and therefore

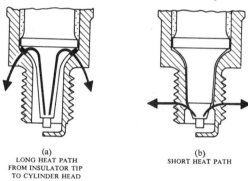

(a)
LONG HEAT PATH
FROM INSULATOR TIP
TO CYLINDER HEAD

(b)
SHORT HEAT PATH

Fig. 12.9 Plug heat range: (a) hot plug; (b) cold plug

retain less heat. Cold plugs are fitted into hot-running engines, and hot plugs into cold-running engines, to obtain the best results.

Construction

The plug consists of a centre electrode made of a metal which can resist both high temperatures, and the chemical action of the combustion and the additives in the petrol. Nickel alloys, platinum, and iridium are used for electrodes. The centre electrode is enclosed by an insulator of aluminium oxide, which is the best ceramic material for resisting temperature variations. All plug insulators are extremely hard and fairly brittle, and must be handled with care, i.e. the correct type of wrench only must be used. The lower part of the insulator is fitted into a steel shell or body which is screwed into the wall of the combustion chamber so that the plug points are correctly positioned in the combustion chamber, i.e. at the point where ignition is required. In some modern plugs the insulator tip is designed to project into the flow of the incoming mixture of petrol and air to help reduce fouling.

The insulator is made pressure-tight in the body by special seals and gaskets, and an external metal gasket is fitted to make the

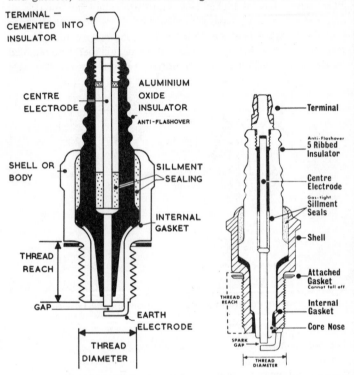

Fig. 12.10 Spark plug   Fig. 12.11 Extended-tip plug

plug a pressure-tight fit in its threaded hole. This external gasket may be slightly crimped to prevent it from falling off the plug. Some plugs have no external gaskets but instead have a bevelled face which seals upon a bevelled face in the plug port. It is important that spark plugs be tightened down to their recommended torque loadings during installation.

An earth electrode is welded to the lower face of the body, and the gap between it and the centre electrode is adjusted by the careful bending of the *earth* electrode only – preferably by the use of a special setting and gapping tool.

Operation
When the very high voltage current is applied to one of the electrodes it is carried across the gap to the other electrode by ionization of the mixture of petrol and air between them. The energy released by the ionization appears as light and heat, i.e. as a spark, the very small and localized area of heat being sufficient to start the burning of the mixture. This small area then heats its surrounding area to the temperature of ignition and the burning spreads throughout the mixture – increasing its temperature and rapidly building up the pressure. The pressure is converted into force by the piston and is exerted upon the crankpin via the connecting rod.

Plug gaps
The gap between the points of the plug must be set, and maintained, accurately. The gap normally increases by about 0·02 mm per 1600 km, due to erosion, and it must be checked and reset at intervals. Both electrode surfaces should be carefully filed to remove accumulated non-conductive glaze and to ensure flat and parallel surfaces. A special tool used for this is illustrated. After sand-blast cleaning the earth electrode only should be carefully

Use of plug, filing, gapping and bending tool

bent to correct the gap, a wire type of feeler gauge being more accurate for this job than the flat strip type of feeler. The recommended gap must be set and this is usually between 0·45 mm and 0·64 mm. Where higher cylinder compression pressures and high voltage coils are employed the electrode gaps of the spark plug may be between 0·76 mm and 1·0 mm.

Excessively wide plug gaps will cause misfiring at high engine speeds. Too small a gap will result in weaker sparks, poor starting, and misfiring. It may also result in the burning of the points of the contact breaker. Too small a gap in a badly worn engine may cause a rapid build-up of deposits of burned oil, and lead to misfiring.

STARTER SYSTEM

The simple starter system consists of a battery, a heavy current-carrying switch which may be hand or foot operated, a starter

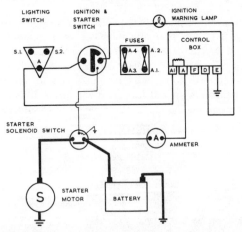

Fig. 12.12 Starter circuit

motor of size suited to the engine, and connecting cables capable of carrying currents of between 300 and 600 amperes. The case of the motor and one terminal post of the battery are earthed, i.e. connected to the chassis.

The modern starter circuit is basically the same, but the manually-operated switch is replaced by a solenoid-operated type. This permits the use of shorter cables and so reduces voltage drop; it is also more convenient. The starter and the ignition switch are incorporated into one unit.

Starter motor
The motor converts electrical energy into mechanical energy, i.e. battery current into torque at the drive gear.

Principles
When a current is passed through a length of wire wound over a soft-iron core the device becomes an electromagnet, the polarity depending upon the direction of the current and the strength of

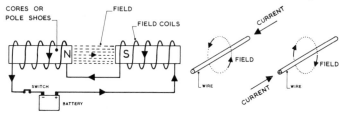

Fig. 12.13 Electromagnetic field   Fig. 12.14 Wire fields

the magnet depending upon the number of turns and the strength of the current. When two such electromagnets are arranged opposite and close to each other, one being of north and the other of south polarity, a magnetic field will be produced in which the lines of force pass straight from one pole to the other.

When a current is passed through a length of wire it produces a magnetic field, the lines of magnetic force tracing circular paths about the centre of the wire. The direction of these forces depends upon the direction of the current, and their strength depends upon the strength of the current. If the wire is bent to form a rectangular loop the direction of the lines of force at one side will be the opposite of those at the other side.

If the loop is so arranged that it can turn about its longitudinal axis, between the poles of the electromagnets, and the current is passed through both the magnet coils and the loop, the magnetic fields of the loop and the magnets will interact. This interaction will result in the magnetic force being strengthened under the left-hand side of the loop and weakened above it. The reverse will occur at the right-hand side and the resulting differences in magnetic pressure will cause the loop to turn clockwise on its axis.

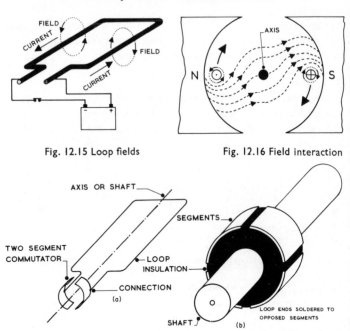

Fig. 12.15 Loop fields   Fig. 12.16 Field interaction

Fig. 12.17 Simple commutation: (a) two-segment; (b) four-segment

When the loop has turned through 180° its field directions are reversed, and the pressure differences would cause it to turn back to its original position. This is prevented by arranging for the direction of its current flow, and of its magnetic fields, to be reversed at this point. The current-reversal device is called a commutator, and in form consists of metal segments, which rotate with the loop, and which pick up the current from two brushes. The action of the commutator makes possible the full and continuous rotation of the loop and its axis (shaft) for as long as the current flows.

Practical construction

In the actual motor the loop is replaced by a number of insulated loops or windings of heavy gauge copper, the ends of which are soldered to insulated, opposed, copper segments. These form the commutator, and the loops pass through slots in a cylindrical, laminated, soft-iron core mounted upon a central steel shaft. This assembly is called the armature, and one end of the shaft carries the drive gear which meshes with the ring gear of the flywheel when the starter is operated.

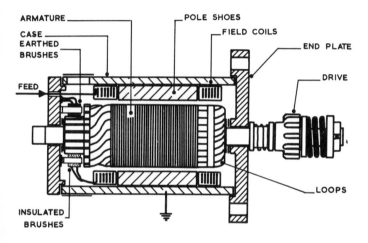

Fig. 12.18 Starter motor in section

The armature is supported by bronze bushes fitted into the end plates of a cylindrical steel case. Inside the case, and surrounding the armature, are four shaped electromagnets or field coils. These are retained by soft-iron pole shoes and are wound to provide alternate north and south poles. The battery current enters the coils at the starter feed terminal and leaves them at two insulated brushes of carbon and copper. The current passes through the armature windings and then to earth via two earthed brushes. The brushes are spring-loaded to contact the commutator and are mounted in holders riveted to the end plate. In most starters the field coils are wound series and parallel, i.e. the current divides after the field terminal to pass through two coils at each side before leaving via the insulated brushes. This reduces the resistance and makes possible greater field strengths – so providing a more powerful motor. In strict classification they are series-wound motors.

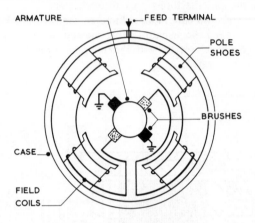

Fig. 12.19 Series-parallel motor

Battery capacity

The size of the battery for a particular vehicle is largely determined by the power required for the proper operation of the starter motor. If the starter motor requires 300 amps at 9 volts to rotate the crankshaft of a cold engine, the battery must be capable of delivering much more power than this. If it cannot, the voltage drop resulting from the operation of the starter will be excessive, and the starter and the ignition system will not function properly.

Starter torques

Lock torque

This is sometimes known as stall torque and is the torque of the starter at the moment the switch contacts are closed. Current flows through the starter but, due to the load, the armature cannot rotate. Lock torque may be tested by a special device which, in principle, is a torque arm and an accurate spring balance.

The ratio of the starter pinion to the ring gear on the flywheel is about 10:1, i.e. the armature torque is multiplied by ten. Engine cranking speeds may be quoted as relating to hot or cold engine conditions and are usually at least 100 revolutions per minute.

Breakaway torque
This is the torque required to initially overcome the compression, inertia, friction, oil drag etc of the engine. It is the greatest demand imposed upon the starter but is short in duration. Series motors are used for starters because they have the characteristic of producing their maximum torque at the beginning of their armature rotation.

Inertia drive
Construction
This is the engagement device used for the starters of most cars and light commercial vehicles. A number of different forms are in service but in all of them the inertia due to the mass of the starter pinion is made use of in the engagement action. Where the pinion moves inwards (towards the starter) to engage with the ring gear on the flywheel the drive is classed as an inboard type. Where the pinion moves away from the starter it is an outboard type, and a third bush has to be provided to support the outer end of the armature shaft. In all starters the float of the shaft end is limited by shim washers fitted between the end-plate faces and shoulders on the shaft. As starters are only used intermittently, bronze bushes are used instead of ball bearings.

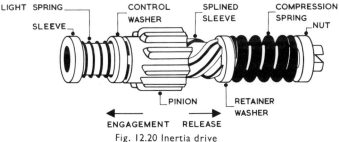

Fig. 12.20 Inertia drive

In the simpler inertia-drive arrangements the armature shaft is splined and has a short threaded portion at the end. The drive itself consists of a shouldered, cylindrical sleeve; a light coil spring which fits over the sleeve; a thick washer to control pinion travel; a sleeve which is splined internally to the armature shaft and which has an external, multi-start, square thread; a pinion with an internal, multi-start, square thread; a thick spring retainer washer; a very strong compression spring; and a spring retainer nut and split pin. These units are assembled on the shaft in the sequence given, the pinion fitting over the sleeve and being held in position by the two washers.

Engagement

When the contacts of the starter motor switch are closed, the armature shaft and the sleeve quickly reach a high speed of rotation. Due to its inertia (weight) the rotation of the pinion is delayed, and this results in its being screwed laterally along the sleeve, compressing the light spring and then being stopped by the control washer. At this point the pinion is forced to rotate with the armature shaft and is fully engaged with the teeth of the ring gear of the flywheel. The shock of engagement forces the sleeve back along the shaft, and is then absorbed by the large compression spring.

Release

As the engine fires and runs, the speed of the flywheel becomes greater than that of the pinion and the armature. The pinion is therefore thrown back out of engagement and the compression spring absorbs the shock of its return.

Special points

The pinion and the sleeve threads must be kept clean, and only the thinnest possible film of thin oil should be used. A dirty or over-lubricated pinion may result in faulty engagement. Other causes of faulty engagement may be broken springs or incorrect out-of-mesh clearance. The light spring is used to prevent the pinion being moved into mesh by vibration when the engine is running.

Failure to release may be due to worn flywheel or pinion teeth, worn drive assembly, a bent armature shaft, or the switch contacts being burned together.

Other drives

The inertia types of drive are not strong enough to enable them to stand up to repeated use with the compression-ignition type of engine. This is because of the large diameter and heavy flywheels, and the much higher compression ratios. Although these engines are fitted with similar starter motors, they have engagement devices in which the pinion must be engaged with the flywheel *before* the armature can be rotated. The pinion may be moved into mesh manually or by means of a solenoid, the closing stages of the engagement also operating the switch contacts to pass current through the motor. Both types are known as pre-engaged starters.

Switches and cables
Switches
The switch for the starter motor is fitted at some convenient point in the circuit between the battery and the starter feed terminal, and it may be manually or solenoid operated. Manual types may be push or pull, or may be foot operated. Essentially these switches all consist of three insulated copper plates, two being connected to the cable and the third bridging the gap between them when required.

In order to avoid voltage losses when passing very heavy currents, the contact plates must be relatively substantial and the make-and-break action must be quick and clean. There must be an adequate open gap and very little arcing. The moving contact is usually a self-centring disc mounted on a spindle and spring cushioned. It is forced away from the fixed contacts by a spring and moved towards them by either a push mechanism or a pull mechanism. The contacts and their mechanism are totally enclosed to keep them dry and clean.

In the solenoid types the moving contact is connected to the solenoid plunger and is drawn down to the fixed contacts as the plunger is drawn into the coil. The switch case must be properly earthed. The advantage of the solenoid switch is that it can be mounted almost anywhere to permit the use of shorter cables for carrying the heavy current cables (less volt drop). The connection to the solenoid from the driver's switch is made by a much lighter cable, and this switch may be combined with the ignition switch, or may be a separate pushbutton type.

Cables
The cables used to connect the battery to the starter motor must

be capable of carrying between 250 and 600 amperes for short periods, and must be well insulated. The voltage drop must be small and the cables must also be protected from mechanical damage. The size chosen depends upon the load imposed upon the starter by the engine when cold. The older cables were covered in rubber, waterproof tape, and braided cotton. Later types are covered by a tough and flexible plastic material. The cables themselves consist of a number of copper wires twisted together. A small car may be fitted with a 37/0·90 mm cable, i.e. a cable consisting of 37 wires each of 0·90 mm diameter. Larger cars may have 61/0·90 mm cables, and commercial vehicles may be fitted with 61/1·10 mm cables.

Connections

Connections in the starter circuit must be both electrically sound and mechanically strong to avoid voltage losses and poor starting. At the battery, the connection may be made either by die-cast or clamped types of lug. In commercial vehicles the lugs are bolted to the battery terminal. These connections particularly, and the battery and engine earth connections, must be kept clean, dry and tight. The cable ends at the starter switch and the motor are usually fitted into large, tubular, plated copper or brass eyelets which are soldered or pressed on to the cables. These connectors are secured to the units by set bolts and lock washers, or by nuts and washers. Many of these cables are available as ready-made replacements.

FAULT DIAGNOSIS

In all vehicle work the essentials of fault location are a good theoretical knowledge and methodical working.

Instruments required

While special equipment is needed to test certain units for correct operation, e.g. distributor dwell-angle testers, the following relatively cheap instruments will enable most circuit faults to be accurately and quickly located. As with most things, practice in their use makes the job easier.

(1) A hydrometer calibrated from 1·130 to 1·300.

(2) A high-rate discharge tester suitable for the batteries most frequently handled.
(3) A moving-coil d.c. voltmeter with a range of 0 to 20 volts (0 to 40 volts for 24-volt systems).
(4) A moving-coil d.c. ammeter calibrated 5–0–50 amps.

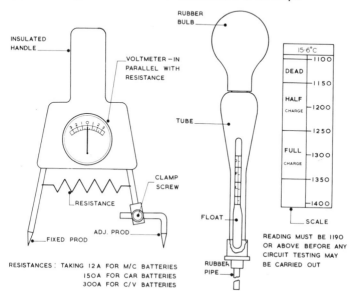

Fig. 12.21 Discharge tester   Fig. 12.22 Hydrometer

Battery checks

In electrical fault-finding the first step is *always* to check the battery for state of charge and cell condition. The state of charge is checked by the use of the hydrometer, the battery having to be at least half charged before any tests can be carried out, i.e. the electrolyte density must give a reading of at least 1·190. If it does not, the battery must be charged by an external charger. If the battery is more than half charged, its condition, i.e. its ability to deliver sufficient current at sufficient voltage to operate the starter, may be checked by the use of the high-rate discharge tester. The battery is in good condition if a steady reading of 1·5 V to 1·6 V can be maintained for about 10 seconds. If the reading falls rapidly the battery must be replaced.

Quick check

If the time or the instruments are not available for a proper check, the battery may be checked by switching on the ignition and the lights, and operating the starter motor. If the lights remain on and the starter functions properly the battery may be considered to be in reasonable condition.

Circuit checking

The two accompanying tables show the sequence of the checks which should be carried out to locate faults in the ignition and the starter circuits.

Table 12.1 Checking the ignition system

	Check made	Result obtained	Conclusion	Remedies
1.	BATTERY for state of charge – hydrometer	Reading above 1·190 Reading below 1·190	State of charge satisfactory State not satisfactory	Recharge battery by external charger
2.	BATTERY for condition high-rate discharge test	Reading of about 1·5 V steady for about 10 seconds Reading falls quickly	Battery condition satisfactory Battery not satisfactory	Replace battery with new unit
3.	PRIMARY CIRCUIT *Voltage to coil* Voltmeter connected to SW or − of coil and to earth. Points of contact breaker *closed* Ignition switched on	Battery voltage shown No voltage shown	This part of circuit correct Open circuit, i.e. complete break in this part circuit	Check cables and connections and rectify
4.	*Voltage from coil* Voltmeter connected to CB of coil and earth. Points of contact breaker *open*. Ignition switched on	Battery voltage shown No voltage shown	Primary winding satisfactory Open circuit in primary winding or short circuit to earth in distributor	Give check 4 (a) to determine which fault it is

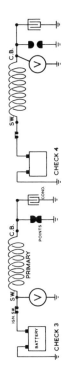

Check made	Result obtained	Conclusion	Remedies
4 (a) Disconnect circuit wire to distributor at CB terminal of coil. Repeat check 4	No voltage shown Battery voltage shown	Open circuit in primary winding Short circuit to earth in distributor	Replace coil by new unit Give check 4 (b) to locate
4 (b) Check in distributor: Wire between CB terminal of coil and distributor terminal Flexible wire terminal to moving contact Wire from terminal to condenser. Presence of insulating washer under moving contact. Condenser shorting to earth			Repairs or replacements as found necessary
5. Voltage from coil Voltmeter connected between CB terminal of coil and earth Points *closed*	No voltage shown Voltage shown	*Primary circuit satisfactory* Dirty contacts or poor earth connections through distributor	Clean contacts and reset Clean contact areas of distributor

No.	Check	Observation	Condition	Action
	at distributor end. Switch on ignition Hold cable end 6 mm from cylinder head Flick points of contact-breaker open	points are opened	condenser both satisfactory	
		No spark at all	Secondary winding or condenser short circuited	Give check 7 to determine which
		Weak spark	Condenser open circuit	Replace condenser with new unit
7.	*Condenser check* Disconnect condenser – connect new unit between LT terminal and earth. Repeat check 6	Good spark each time points opened	Original condenser faulty	Replace by new unit
		No spark at all	Secondary winding faulty	Replace by new coil
8.	*Rotor arm check* Place end of HT cable 3 mm from metal of arm. Flick points of contact breaker open	Spark does not jump to arm	Rotor arm insulation sound	
		Spark each time points open	Insulation unsound – minute puncture – spark to camshaft	Replace by new unit
9.	*Cap and HT cable check* Clean and dry cap Examine for tracking, cracks, signs of burning	None visible	Cap insulation and condition satisfactory	
		Some faults observed	Cap not satisfactory	Replace by new unit
	Examine HT cables for cracks chafing, oil soaking	None visible	Cables satisfactory	
		Some faults observed	Cables not satisfactory *Complete ignition circuit satisfactory*	Replace by new cables and connectors

Table 12.2 Checking the starter system

Check made	Result obtained	Conclusion	Remedies
1. *Battery* for state of charge – hydrometer test	Reading above 1·190	State of charge satisfactory	Recharge battery on bench
	Reading below 1·190	State of charge not satisfactory	
2. *Battery* for condition – high-rate discharge test	Reading of about 1·5 V steady for 10 seconds	Battery condition satisfactory	Replace by new unit
	Reading falls quickly	Battery not satisfactory	
3. *Voltage at battery* Connect voltmeter across battery terminal posts Close starter switch	Reading 10 V or more in 12 V petrol system Reading 8·5 V or more in 12 V diesel system Reading 4·5 V or more in 6 V petrol system	Battery voltage satisfactory	Recharge or replace unit
	Reading less than above	Battery voltage not satisfactory	
4. *Voltage across starter motor* Connect voltmeter between feed terminal of starter and casing. Close starter switch. Readings should be not more than 0·5 V below those obtained in check 3	Low voltage readings in checks 3 and 4	Motor taking excessive current	Replace or strip and rebuild
	Low voltage in check 4 only	High resistance in cable	Check cable size and all connections. Check 5.
	Voltage falls quickly	Discharged or faulty battery	Recharge or replace unit

273

5. *Voltage drop in feed cable*
Connect voltmeter between battery and feed terminals of starter

Switch contacts open	Battery voltage	Feed cable satisfactory
Switch contact closed	Reading less than 0·5 V	Feed cable satisfactory
	Reading more than 0·5 V	Excessive resistance in cable – probably connections or switch contacts at fault

Check connections for dirt and security. Check 6

6. *Volt drop in switch*
Connect voltmeter across switch terminals

Switch contacts open	Battery voltage	Switch satisfactory
Switch contacts closed	No voltage shown, or less than 0·5 V	Switch satisfactory
	Voltage more than 0·5 V	Switch contacts probably burned

Replace with new unit

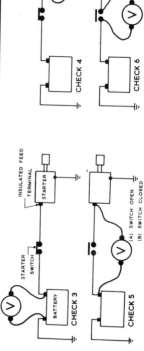

274

Check made	Result obtained	Conclusion	Remedies
7. *Voltage drop in earth side of starter* Connect voltmeter between earthed terminal of battery and starter case. Close switch contacts	Reading falls to zero as contacts are closed	Earth side satisfactory – within 0·5 V limit	Clean and retighten
	Reading above zero	Resistance of earth connection excessive – dirt, paint, corrosion	
8. *Engine earth connections* Check for security, corrosion, paint, damage, metal-to-metal contact	Clean, tight, metal contact	Earth connections satisfactory	*Starter circuit satisfactory*
	Any of the faults found	Earth connections faulty	Clean, dry and remake metal-to-metal contacts

CHECK 7

THE NIFE/ALCAD BATTERY

This is the trade name for the Nickel Cadmium Alkaline battery manufactured by Alkaline Batteries Ltd., and marketed by Joseph Lucas (Batteries). These batteries are used in PSV types of vehicle and in special types of vehicle, such as bulk milk transporters. Each cell is a separate unit with a voltage of about 1·25 volts when fully charged. In a 12-volt battery, nine cells are connected in series; eighteen cells form a 24-volt battery. For insulating purposes the cells are fitted into special wooden cases.

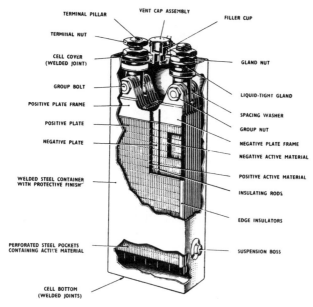

Each cell consists of a deep, rectangular, rust-proofed container which has a welded cover plate. The plate is fitted with a gas-vented and spring-loaded filler cup and cap. The cell plates take the form of finely perforated steel envelopes which enclose the chemically active materials. In the positive plates these are nickel hydroxide and graphite, and in the negative plates are cadmium oxide, together with a special oxide of iron. Each plate has a lug by which it is bolted to its collecting bar, there being one more positive plate than there are negative plates in the cell grouping. This gives a positive plate at each end of the grouping. Because the outsides of these plates contact the container, they have, in effect, only half the capacity, i.e. these two plates are equivalent to a single positive plate and this gives the correct balance to the cell. The cell container is therefore at positive potential.

The plates are separated by PVC rods of small diameter, and the upper ends of the bars are sealed at the cover plate by rubber glands. The outer ends of the bars are threaded and are provided with nuts of large contact area to hold the lugs of connecting cables, and/or intercell or intercrate connectors, in position.

The electrolyte is a chemically pure solution of potassium hydroxide which both assists the chemical changes in the cell and helps to preserve the steel surfaces. This electrolyte must not be exposed to the atmosphere or its purity will be destroyed.

Chemical action
Charge
When a charging current is passed through the cell, the cadmium oxide of the negative plates is converted into pure cadmium while the nickel hydroxide of the positive plates is converted into higher oxide of nickel. In simple terms the passage of the charging current causes oxygen atoms to be released by the cadmium. These atoms are then combined with the nickel via the medium of the electrolyte. *The electrolyte itself is unchanged*; it merely assists in the transfer of the oxygen atoms. As both oxygen and hydrogen are set free by the chemical actions gassing is not a guide to the completion of the charge.

Discharge
When the battery supplies current the nickel hydroxide of the positive plates releases oxygen atoms, leaving a lower oxide of nickel. The released atoms are then combined with the cadmium of the negative plates to form cadmium oxide. Once again the electrolyte itself is unchanged and only assists in the transfer of the atoms.

Electrolyte
The specific gravity (density) of the electrolyte may be between

1·200 and 1·160 at normal temperature. A fall in the level of the electrolyte will be due to evaporation or spillage, and must be corrected by adding distilled water. In general, high gravities should be avoided – particularly when associated with high temperatures. The combination of these two factors is likely to damage the active materials. Very low gravities should also be avoided because these may cause damage to the negative plate.

The level of the electrolyte should be maintained at about one inch above the top of the plates. This should be checked against the information given in the handbook supplied with each battery, and the level corrected with a filling apparatus and checked with a simple, graduated, level-testing tube available for this purpose.

Charging current

The normal charge rate is (rated capacity of the battery in ampere hours divided by 5) amperes for 7 hours. This will restore a fully discharged battery to the fully charged state, i.e. a discharged 100 ampere/hour battery is fully recharged by charging at 20 amperes for 7 hours. The battery is considered discharged when the cell voltage has fallen to 1·1 volts per cell on load.

Note that these batteries are not harmed by overcharging. They will also withstand occasional overdischarging. Overdischarged batteries should be recharged at the normal rate for twice the normal time.

Special points

(1) The essential difference between the alkaline and the lead-acid batteries is that the electrolyte in the alkaline battery *only assists* in the chemical actions – it is not changed itself.

(2) Plate shedding cannot occur in the alkaline battery because the active materials are enclosed in the perforated steel envelope.

(3) The alkaline electrolyte has a preservative effect upon the materials of the cells.

Advantages of alkaline battery

(1) It is mechanically very strong because of its all-steel construction.

(2) Provided that the necessary and simple routine maintenance procedures are carried out, it has a very long life, e.g. 15 to 20 years on buses – the life of the vehicle itself.

(3) It can be left in any state of charge, including fully discharged, for very long periods without deterioration and with only negligible loss of charge.

(4) It is not damaged by overcharging, nor by an accidental short circuit.

(5) For most applications the electrolyte need be changed only once or twice during the life of the battery. For commercial vehicles changing every three years is recommended.

(6) The terminals do not corrode.

Disadvantages

(1) Higher initial cost.

(2) Efficiency is 70–75% ampere/hours or 60–65% watt/hours. (This is not a real disadvantage in most applications.)

Advantages of lead-acid battery

(1) Relatively cheap.

(2) Efficiency 80–90% ampere/hours or 70–75% watt/hours. (This is an advantage in some applications.)

Disadvantages

(1) Requires more careful and regular servicing.

(2) Charge and discharge rates must be controlled to avoid destroying the battery.

(3) It must never be left in a discharged state.

(4) Life is only about two or three years. This usually is equivalent to about 225 charges and discharges.

Further points

(a) Low-resistance alkaline batteries are comparable to lead-acid types in internal resistance, and their resistance increases less on discharge.

(b) The capacity of the alkaline battery is less reduced by low temperatures than that of the lead-acid battery. There is also no risk of the alkaline battery suffering damage from freezing of the electrolyte.

Appendix

The SI System of Units

Most countries are now abandoning their traditional systems of measurement, in which units often have no logical relationship, and are adopting the modern form of the metric system – the Système Internationale d'Unites (SI system). The units of this system can be defined accurately and universally, and the multiples and sub-multiples of all the units are logically arranged in steps of ten.

Many designers are now using SI units for their calculations and dimensions, many manufacturers are using them in their production systems, and servicing requirements are coming to be expressed in them. The changeover is naturally taking some time and it is necessary during this changeover period for motor mechanics to use both SI units and the 'imperial' units which have been customarily used in Britain and the Commonwealth.

Under the SI system, clearances and settings are specified in millimetres, petrol is supplied by the litre, speedometers are calibrated in kilometres per hour, and tyre pressures are specified in newtons per square metre or related units. Everyone must therefore learn to think in SI units – to visualize, for example, a millimetre – and to use decimal fractions with accuracy and speed.

The SI system has six basic units – the metre (m) for length, the kilogram (kg) for mass, the second (s) for time, the ampere (A) for electric current, the degree Kelvin* (K) for absolute temperature and the candela (cd) for luminous intensity. All other SI units are derived from these; thus the unit of area is the square metre (m^2), the unit of acceleration is metre per second per second (m/s^2), and the unit of pressure is newton per square metre (N/m^2), the newton being the force which when applied to a body of unit mass (1 kg) gives it unit acceleration (m/s^2).

Basic units may be multiplied or divided by a ten-based factor,

* Temperature is ordinarily measured in degrees Celsius (°C).

denoted by the use of prefixes as in the metric system. The most
commonly used prefixes are:

Prefix	Symbol	Unit multiplied by:	Example
mega	M	one million (10^6)	megawatt (MW)
kilo	k	one thousand (10^3)	kilometre (km)
hecto	h	one hundred (10^2)	hectogram (hg)
deca	da	ten (10^1)	decagram (dag)
		Unit divided by:	
deci	d	ten (10^{-1})	decimetre (dm)
centi	c	one hundred (10^{-2})	centimetre (cm)
milli	m	one thousand (10^{-3})	millimetre (mm)
micro	μ	one million (10^{-6})	micrometre or micron (μm)

A sub-unit of particular interest to mechanics is the cubic decimetre (dm^3) for which the new system allows use of the term 'litre'
for ordinary purposes such as petrol measurement, although not
for precise measurements; the litre is minutely larger than the
cubic decimetre (1·000028).

Tables and slide rules for conversions to and from SI units are
becoming readily available, and only representative values are
given below. Mechanics are advised, however, to make themselves
familiar with the general basis of the SI system (including symbols
and abbreviations) and to become proficient at more complicated
conversions.

Length

0·001 in	= 0·0254 mm	1 mm	= 0·0394 in
$\frac{1}{64}$ in	= 0·3969 mm	1 cm	= 0·3937 in
1 in	= 25·4 mm	1 m	= 3·2808 ft
1 ft	= 0·3048 m		= 1·0936 yd
1 yd	= 0·9144 m	1 km	= 0·6214 mile
1 mile	= 1·6093 km		

Area

1 in²	= 6·4516 cm²	1 mm²	= 0·0015 in²
1 ft²	= 0·0929 m²	1 cm²	= 0·1550 in²
1 yd²	= 0·8361 m²	1 m²	= 10·764 ft² (1·196 yd²)
1 mile²	= 2·5899 km²	1 km²	= 0·386 mile²

Volume

1 in³	= 16·387 cm³	1 cm³ =	0·061 in³
1 ft³	= 0·0283 m³	1 m³ =	35·315 ft³
1 yd³	= 0·7646 m³	1 m³ =	1·3079 yd³

Capacity

1 pint	= 0·5682 litre	1 litre = 0·2199 gallon
1 quart	= 1·1365 litre	1 litre = 0·2642 US gallon
1 gallon	= 4·5461 litre	
1 US gallon	= 3·785 litre	

Mass

1 oz =	28·349 g	1 gm = 0·0353 oz
1 lb =	0·4536 kg	1 kg = 2·2046 lb
1 cwt =	50·802 kg	1 t* = 0·984 ton
1 ton =	1016·05 kg	
1 ton =	1016·05 kg	
=	1·016 tonne (t*)	

* The abbreviation t should be used only for tonne (equivalent to former metric ton) and not for ton.

Density

1 lb/in³ =	27·679 Mg/m³	1 kg/m³ = 0·06243 lb/ft³
=	27·679 g/cm³	
1 lb/ft³ =	16·018 kg/m³	
1 ton/yd³ =	1328·94 kg/m³	
=	1·2389 t/m³	
1 lb/gal =	99·7763 kg/m³	

Velocity

1 ft/s	= 0·3048 m/s	1 m/s = 3·2808 ft/s
1 mile/h	= 1·6093 km/h	1 km/h = 0·6214 mile/h

Acceleration

1 ft/s² = 0·3048 m/s²	1 m/s² = 3·280 ft/s²

Force

1 lbf = 4·4482 N	1 N = 0·2248 lbf
1 tonf = 9964 N	1 kgf = 9·8066 N

Torque

1 lbf ft	= 1·356 N m	1 N m = 0·7376 lbf ft	
1 lbf in	= 0·1130 N m		

Pressure and stress

1 lbf/in²	= 6894·76 N/m²	1 kgf/mm²	= 0·6349 tonf/in²
	= 0·0703 kgf/cm²		
		1 kgf/cm²	= 14·2233 lbf/in²
1 tonf/in² =	1·5749 kgf/mm²	1 N/m²	= 145·038 × 10⁶
	15·4443 MN/m²		lbf/in²
			= 64·749 × 10⁻⁹
			tonf/in²

Energy

1 ft lbf	= 1·8556 J (joule)	1 J = 0·7376 ft lbf
1 hp h	= 2·6845 MJ	
1 Btu	= 1·055 kJ	**Power**
1 therm	= 105·506 MJ	1 ft lbf/s = 1·3558 W (watt)
1 kWh	= 3·6 MJ	1 hp = 745·7 W
1 calorie	= 4·1868 J	1 metric hp = 735·5 W

The joule (J) is the work done when the point of application of a force of one newton is displaced through a distance of one metre in the direction of the force (i.e. J = 1 N m); the watt (W) is the unit of power equivalent to one joule per second (W = J/s).

Index